WOOL

UNIVERSITY
GEOLOGICAL
DEPARTMENT
COLLEGE

By permission of] *[the British Australasian.*

AN AUSTRALIAN FLOCK.

PITMAN'S COMMON COMMODITIES OF COMMERCE

WOOL

FROM THE RAW MATERIAL TO THE FINISHED PRODUCT

BY

J. A. HUNTER

LONDON
SIR ISAAC PITMAN & SONS, LTD., 1 AMEN CORNER, E.C.
BATH AND NEW YORK
1912?

PRINTED BY SIR ISAAC PITMAN & SONS, LTD., LONDON, BATH, AND NEW YORK

PREFACE

It is in broad terms true to say that cotton is the clothing of the East and wool the clothing of the West. Cotton forms the staple of attire in the hot and backward countries. Wool is the chief covering of dwellers in more temperate climes, and of those in general who have adopted Western standards of comfort. In a rather special sense wool is at once a measure and a signal of the advance of modern civilisation.

Some comparison with cotton and with other industries is necessary to a right perspective of the place occupied by wool in the general economy of the world. Cotton clothes more persons and is manufactured on a greater scale. Cotton is the largest of textile industries, but wool is next. Agriculture, building, coal-mining, and cotton, among the great primary trades of this country employ more people; but in limiting the survey to manufactures one is doing something less than justice to wool.

Wool-growing, or, to be more precise, sheep-farming, is a very important part of the vast industry of agriculture, and in these Islands probably the most important part of all. The sheep is the pivot of British farming, and the wool-bearing animal out-numbers any other quadrupedal farming stock by nearly three to one. The relation of the sheep to farming and to the wool manufacturing industry will be considered in more detail later on. Let it suffice here to note that British farming entails the constant use of some 30,000,000 sheep.

The manufacture of wool is carried on upon one scale or another in nearly all countries, and employs more persons in this country than in any. Handsomely more than one quarter-million people draw their livelihood directly from the British manufacturing industry. Round the wool manufactures cluster a large ring of subsidiary trades, and the industry supplies the life's blood to four at least of the largest towns in the country.

The history of wool over a number of centuries is virtually the history of British commerce. From the earliest times wool or wool goods have formed a great part of England's foreign trade, and the utilisation of wool for clothing goes back to the depths of antiquity.

In all ages, British wool and woollens have enjoyed a high reputation for excellence in the penetrable parts of the outer world. The manufacture is one in which our people have developed a marked special aptitude, and "English" or, it may be, "Scotch" remains the highest commendation the foreign tailor can bestow on the cloth he exhibits to his customer. The respect shown to those names is not diminishing, and although representatives of all nations come here to learn British methods, and although British machinery is used largely by them, the learners do not surpass the tutor.

Many matters of practice in connection with the industry are difficult to communicate. Wool is a material to be humoured rather than driven, and the processes through which it goes involve the use of patience and experience as well as understanding. The operations can be no more than outlined in a book of these dimensions, which, so far as it goes, aims at giving a bird's-eye presentment of wool and its industries in all their parts.

CONTENTS

LIST OF ILLUSTRATIONS

WOOL

CHAPTER I

WOOL AND SHEEP

THERE are in the world at present probably some five to six hundred million head of sheep. The total is not one about which precise information is procurable. Censuses of live stock are of doubtful accuracy at best, and from some countries none is forthcoming, while in others the count is made irregularly, or only at intervals of several years. The estimates are thus approximations merely, and liable to be coloured to suit particular sets of views. Accepting as independent the statistics put forward by the United States Census of Agriculture (1908) we get a world's total of 593,976,000 sheep. As wool supplies are reckoned rather by bales of wool received at ports than by the head of sheep, the possible inaccuracies of the statement need not concern us. Similarly the details from the same source showing the distribution in round numbers of sheep by continents need only be taken as overhead figures.

Europe and United Kingdom ..	185	million head.
Australia and New Zealand ..	109	,, ,,
Asia	91	,, ,,
Africa	46	,, ,,
North America	64	,, ,,
South America	99	,, ,,

The sheep of the world are found as far north as Iceland and as far south as the Magellan Strait, with the north and south temperate zones as their chief *habitat.* They extend into the semi-tropics, but only the highest altitudes in the tropical zone afford congenial surroundings for producers either of good mutton or good wool. In numbers, and, to a smaller extent, in areas of distribution, there is a more or less continual change. In Europe, which remains the chief sheep-raising (although not the chief wool-producing) continent, the number dwindles. There has been a loss, according to Messrs. Dalgety's tables, of twenty-one million European sheep in fourteen years. In Australasia, the otherwise continuous production of sheep is checked by such droughts as that which lasted eight years and ended in 1902. In Argentina the introduction of grain growing and the increased rental crushes sheep southward into the colder country, Patagonia. In North America the closer settlement and the profit from grain restrict the development of sheep farming. South Africa, which is regarded now as the coming wool country, and Siberia, are both adopting enlightened methods of sheep culture, and both likely to produce more and better wool.

Naturally, in lands as far apart as these, the considerations which prompt agriculturists are various. The circumstances of farmers much nearer differ radically, but the sheep, despite differences of breed and country, is in one respect the same. It yields a double harvest, in mutton and in wool. The pastoralist in the grass lands of Australia, Argentina, South Africa, or any other country of uncertain rainfall, might, if he chose, pasture cattle on his run. They would be longer in coming to maturity, and hence in turning crops into cash. They would have a greater value per head, and expose him to more risk in case of deaths in the herd. They would require more water, and not be fat for market in dry seasons. A very substantial reason for placing sheep on a pasture fit for other animals is that it divides the farming risk.

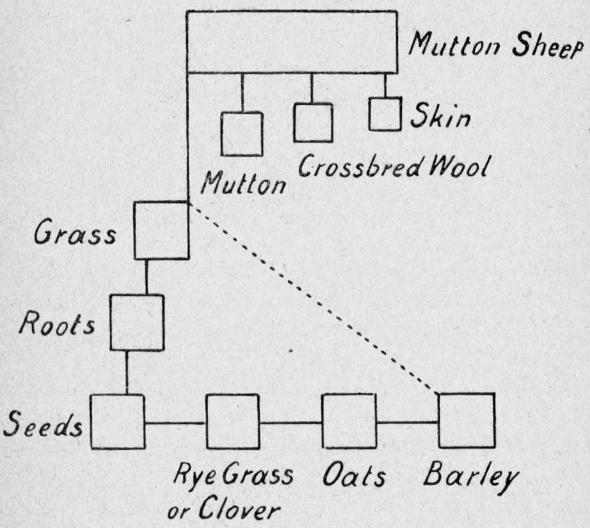

THE PRODUCE OF THE MUTTON SHEEP IN HUSBANDRY

The advantage is more complex, but no less clear, in the case of the "mixed" farmer working both grass and arable land. To him also the sheep provides both wool and meat, but its services are further-reaching. The sheep is a great clearer and improver of pastures, a provider of more and sweeter grass for other stock. Its manure is peculiarly rich, and indispensable in starting and maintaining the English rotation of crops. No terms of enthusiasm are unjustified in commending the part played by the sheep in transmuting grass into corn. A farmer with land which he wishes to make arable, ploughs it and sows a crop of roots. When the turnips ripen he folds his weaned lambs or hoggets on them. The hoggs eat, return their droppings to earth, and tread in and distribute them automatically, to the saving of labour. By the time the root crop is done, the hoggs are ready for shearing and to return their first yield in the price of wool. They are fat and ready for the fat lamb market, where their carcasses fetch so much a pound. The turnip field is ripe next for a crop of seed grass which should sustain lambs, and their milking mothers at the rate of five to eight to the acre from April to October. In the following year rye-grass is sown along with clover, and there is more rich grazing as well as a yield of hay. Oats follow and next barley, and the cycle begins again and continues endlessly without impoverishment of the soil. The animal which makes this farming magic possible is the sheep which in England gives not only wool and mutton but also corn.

In mixed farming the sheep is the great economist and the keep of a ewe costs in this country from 3d. to 5d. a week. A lamb and a ewe of Hampshire Down breed cost, on Professor Wrightson's calculation, some 30s. a year gross, and perhaps 26s. net when the value of the wool has been deducted. To pay for these and leave a profit there is the ewe's lamb, whose price is governed by the market. There is more than one lamb per ewe ; out of 1,000 ewes of the breed in point, there should be reared and ready for market 1,100 lambs. Assuming a price for lambs that is neither the lowest nor the highest known, allowing for labour 1d. per head per week, and another 1d. for risks and expenses, Professor Wrightson's calculations show a profit of £2 per ewe, which in his case is the same as

£2 per acre. The residuals in the land, the benefit to pasture currently and to succeeding crops are additional to the profit named. The cost of keeping sheep varies with a score of different factors, of which rent, food, and labour are only a few. The matter is one on which pastoralists show reticence, for some of them do not wish consumers to know the terms upon which farming for wool can be made to pay. Some U.S. Government enquiries made in Utah, suggest that the cost per head for grazing, herding, feeding, shearing, dipping, lambing, carriage on wool and mutton, and interest is about 6s. 3d. The sum is unlikely to be understated, and the same is the case with the general estimate that merino wool can be produced on the large Australian sheep runs at 5d. per lb. The yield of wool per animal might be anything between five pounds and ten, according to the season, district, and quality of sheep. Sixpence per lb. is stated by the American Tariff Board to be the average cost of raising fine merino wool in the United States. In Ohio the cost is said not to be less than 9½d. In the Western States fine crossbred is said to cost the producer at least 5½d., and the average cost of producing coarse and fine wool is estimated at 4¾d. for the whole country. The report adds that in South America the corresponding cost is 2d. to 2½d. per lb. In making up these figures the American Tariff Board treated wool as the sole product of the sheep to the disregard of mutton and tallow and the improvement of pastures. The data are too indefinite to shape a positive opinion as to the net cost per animal, but in view of the mean price of Australian greasy merino wool over a period of years, it is clear that wool produced at or near 5d. realises a good profit. The mean prices on the next page are taken from Messrs. H. Schwartze & Co.'s list.

	Highest.	Lowest.	Mean.
Australian Port Phillip	(1899) 15½	(1895) 7½	11½d. per lb.
,, Sydney average greasy short	,, 13	,, 6	9½ ,,
,, Adelaide average greasy short	,, 11	,, 5	8 ,,
New Zealand super greasy short	,, 15	,, 7½	11½ ,,

The table is witness to the fluctuations that occur in wool, sometimes with startling suddenness, and it is continued to show the variations in prices of some other qualities :—

	Highest.	Lowest.	Mean.
Australian Crossbred super greasy fine	(1909) 17	(1901) 9	13d. per lb.
Cape Eastern Merino average fleece	(1895) 14	(1895) 6½	10¼ ,,
Buenos Ayres average greasy 36%	,, 9½	,, 4⅜	7 ,,
English Lincoln hoggs ..	,, 16½	(1902) 7¼	11⅞ ,,
Mohair, Turkish fair average	,, 32	(1892) 12	22 ,,

Were the profit less large, it would at least be early, and the farmer must of necessity value the quickness as well as the size of his returns. In this country, sheep are kept partly because nothing pays better, partly because to make a change from the system of which the sheep is the keystone must involve a ruinous capital loss to farmers. If they wished, they could not without wasting the fruit of years, copy Denmark, and put farming upon a basis of which the cow should be the foundation. Flocks may, and will, fluctuate in number in countries where mixed farming is pursued, but there is no serious likelihood of the extinction of the sheep in them. Where the unthrifty one-crop system of agriculture is practised, sheep dwindle and are relegated to the bare grounds, the badly-watered lands, the ranges far away from the railway. In Ontario they are bought in small numbers as a "flying flock," and penned on a pasture to eat away the tough grass and weeds distasteful to cattle, and are then sold again. In the Eastern States of America sheep are little kept, apparently because of the high price brought by grain and the nuisance of shed-feeding during winter.

Sheep farming in the neighbourhood of towns and villages suffer discouragement from dogs, and in industrial districts somewhat from smoke, but, given freedom from great climatic extremes, with grass, water, and dry ground, one breed or another of sheep will thrive there with ordinary attention. Our own country provides instances of the extraordinary adaptability of sheep. The Scotch black-faced mountain sheep, valued for its sweet mutton rather than for its coarse carpet-making wool, are found alive but emaciated after three, four, and five weeks' burial in a snowdrift. When the shepherd is at length able to dig them out he finds that they have subsisted upon their own breast-wool and such portions of heather and heather-root as could be reached without moving more than their heads.

Differences of size, appearance, hardiness and suitability to local conditions appear between every two breeds of sheep, and these are accompanied by marked differences in the quantity and character of the wool borne. In the United Kingdom we have highland and lowland sheep; short woolled animals of which Down sheep are the generic type, and long-woolled ones like the Leicester and Lincoln. The wools range in length from three to four inches, when they are suitable chiefly for flannel and hosiery, up to fifteen inches long, when their suitability is determined by their characteristics of coarseness and lustre. The coarsest wools are at least seventy times thicker in diameter than the finest, and in curliness, softness, and colour, there are most conspicuous differences. The variations are vital in determining the manufacturing uses, and in this country, where sheep are kept for mutton more than wool, are of greater concern to the manufacturer than the farmer.

The breeding of pure types of the best English sheep is carried on as well for home as export purposes. Lincolns, Leicesters, Southdowns, Romneys, Wensleydales, Shropshires, Dorsets, Oxfords, and Cheviots, out from England, mingle their blood with merino and local sheep in nearly all countries. Each breed has its own votaries who are grouped into associations, each with its own flock-book and rules for the registration of stock and tabulation of prices and exports.

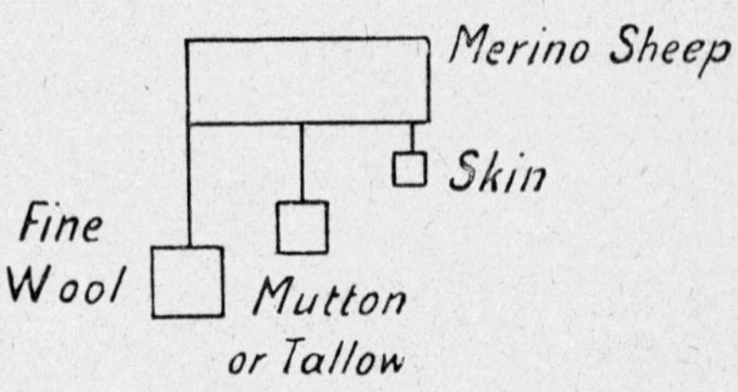

THE PRODUCE OF THE MERINO SHEEP

The Southdown Sheep Club has records covering more than a hundred years, and Southdown rams now alive have a lineage directly traceable through twenty generations. These aristocrats of the English sheep family descend in direct line from ante-Norman times, and not impossibly from the days of the Roman Invasion. They are bearers of the nearest English equivalent to pure merino wool.

The merino sheep, the bearer of the very finest wool, ranging in fineness up to $\frac{1}{3500}$ths of an inch, and woolled so closely that there are from 40,000 to 48,000 fibres per square inch of skin, is of the type that is not grown for the sake of its mutton. The carcass is small,

A PRIZE SOUTHDOWN RAM

the lamb comes to maturity relatively late, and the fat is strong in flavour, but the merino has many virtues. It is an industrious feeder and requires little water, and, unlike the English sheep, can be housed in sheds in winter without contracting serious ailments. The merino is not farmed in England, but directly and indirectly it provides the bulk of the commercial supply of the world's desirable wool. The merino has laid the fortune of Australia and New Zealand, is the rising hope of pastoral South Africa, and the refining influence in the South American wool production. It originates from Spain, and gave Spanish cloth its mediæval reputation. In Spain the purity of the blood has been preserved zealously for centuries, and until comparatively recent times the exportation of merino sheep was a felony punishable with death.

George III secured a few merinos by way of a present, and eight of them, bought and carried to Australia by Captain John Macarthur, are the forefathers of the vast Australian flocks of the day. They were followed by a stud of Saxon merinos, and have at various dates been succeeded by merinos of the Rambouillet, Negretti, and Vermont types. The breed has been modified by life under Australian conditions until the Australian merino has become the standard of the world. In Australia the pure merino grown primarily for its wool, is more largely farmed, and, on the whole, better farmed, than anywhere. The Australian sheep-raising industry is undergoing changes, the full effect of which remains to be seen.

The land policy of the Government involves the break-up of large estates, on which flocks numbering 100,000 and more have been controlled by an individual owner. The transfer of these lands to relatively small holders brings about a diminution in the size of the

SHEEP OFF THE SHEARS, NEW ZEALAND

average flock. The average size in New South Wales, where more than half of Australian wool is grown, in 1910 was some 1,800. Out of 25,500 flocks, some 6,000 were under one hundred, and 7,000 more under five hundred in number. The movement is accompanied by some diminution also in the total number of sheep, and necessarily by some falling off in the quality and preparation of the wool. The small farmer with other claims on his attention, and working on an altogether smaller scale, cannot systematise his business as thoroughly as the great squatters he replaced. The bulk of the New South Wales production is still in large hands, *i.e.*, in those of men with 5,000 sheep and over, but the trend away from the great aggregations of the past is quick and unmistakable. The Australian flocks are still larger upon the average than those of Argentina, where 550 is the mean size, 300 is a small flock, and 3—4,000 a very large one.

On the one hand, the demands of the world for fine wool, and on the other the facilities which bring the frozen carcass of a sheep from New Zealand to London for a bagatelle of ½d. or so per pound, have led to an extensive crossing of the pure merino blood. Macarthur, by crossing the scraggy Bengalese sheep which he found in Australia, contrived to raise the weight of fleeces from some 3½ lbs. to 5 lbs. about a century ago, and since then the average weight of the Australian fleece on some runs has been brought to 12 pounds. Merinos crossed with the short-woolled Southdown, the long-woolled Lincoln, Border-Leicester, or other sheep, are all generically called crossbred. New Zealand sheep are nearly all crossbred, and the same is true of Argentina. Australia and Uruguay are the more important homes of the pure merinos, and in South Africa, by a process of breeding up, the wool comes to approach more uniformly to a pure merino type. Crossbred wool is in all circumstances coarser than pure merino; in some cases so little coarser that the wool is almost merino; and, where crossing has been carried further, so coarse that the wool is scarcely distinguishable from that of its long-woolled English parentage.

The merino is to the sheep what the Arab thoroughbred is to horses, and the crossbred shows at least as many variations of breed as horses do. But imperfect as the classification is, it marks a dividing line through the industry. The worsted industry is divided substantially into two branches, "Botany" (merino) and crossbred, and in general the manufacturer who works the one does not work the other. The wools are different in character, but there is a certain enmity between them. For two or three seasons Botany, to use its Yorkshire name, or Saxony—to give fine wool its Scottish name—is in fashion and crossbred (Cheviot) is out of fashion. This is not to say that consumption of either can or does stop, but for some economic or other reason public taste takes a turn and prefers hard fabrics to soft ones. Crossbred is always the cheaper of the two, and there is a tendency, which is at times disturbed, to maintain a certain average margin of price between them. The prices fluctuate in sympathy or out of sympathy accordingly as demand and supply vary, and there has been an occasion on which crossbred wool was as low in price as American cotton. In 1905 it was gloomily prophesied that coarse wool must for ever stay at or about the cotton price, and that wool from the mutton sheep had become and would remain an inconsiderable by-product. Since then the world has seen bad prices for frozen lamb, and a rise of 150 % in the wool from the animal.

The precise extent of the wool supply, like the exact number of the world's sheep, is a matter on which there is room at least for differences of opinion. The proportion of wool that is grown and retained for local consumption in the remotest parts of the world can profitably be disregarded in calculating the extent of the available resources. The wool that reaches the ports is that which practically matters, and the wool grown in or imported into England, Europe, North America represents the industrial supply. By consulting an infinity of sources, it is possible to arrive at a total for oneself, but difficulty is encountered in reducing the amount to a clean or net basis. Without intimate knowledge of the condition and character of the clip in different years, and without more data than official returns give, the soundness of any conclusion is uncertain. Something is left to opinion, and opinions are not equally authoritative. That of Messrs. Helmuth, Schwartze & Co. is accepted as thoroughly informed, and their statistics, compiled for a long series of years, give the clearest statement obtainable of the quantity of clean wool put at the service of the European and North American industries, and this is shown in relation to the population of the two continents. The calculations show for the decades :—

	lb.	
1861-70	2·26	per head.
1871-80	2·43	,,
1881-90	2·57	,,
1891-1900	2·76	,,
1901-1909	2·64	,,

In other words, after a steady increase during thirty years, supplies are beginning to fail, despite the concurrent increase in production. Persons in the principal wool-using and wool-manufacturing countries multiply more rapidly than sheep, and unless checked by developments on one hand or the other, the process can only have one effect on the prices realised for wool.

The sheep is the great provider, but in addition to wool from the sheep is wool from the goat. Mohair, a long, lustrous, silky wool to which the nearest native equivalent is pure Wensleydale wool, comes from Turkey and South Africa, and is grown to a smaller extent in California. Mohair is the produce of the angora, and the alpaca, with which it is popularly confused, is from the Peruvian llama. Aside from the fact that mohair is finer and more expensive, it is white or nearly white; alpaca is coloured brown or black, with a very small proportion of white occurring in patches. Even the camel yields hair like enough to wool to be worked by similar processes, but the supply is small. The camel is rather an ally than a competitor, and the vicuna llama is to be regarded in the same light. The common goat, and the coarse-haired Persian and East Indian sheep, supply a very different market from the home or colonial sheep, but these wools and hairs come into industry. Goats have a separate habit from the sheep. Not for them the rich grass of meadows; they are at home on the hills and thrive on the picking of scrub and bushes.

CHAPTER II

THE WOOL INDUSTRIES

"A FAIR business is passing in 60's, little is doing in qualities between 50's and 56's, and Topmakers report that their whole production of 40's to 46's is sold."—*Extract from a Bradford market report.*

Numbers like those in the quoted passage appear and reappear whenever wool is mentioned, and in this instance denote the quality of tops (*i.e.*, long wool scoured of grease and combed free of its shortest fibres). The numbers shield the identity of the more familiar names, merino and crossbred. Sixties are the typical merino, forties the medium crossbred, and fifties and fifty-sixes are the fine crossbreds approaching to merino in quality. Manifestly, in one pound of wool of fine diameter there is a greater aggregate length of fibre than in a pound of thicker stuff. Other things equal it is clear that in a pound of yarn spun to the practicable limit of fineness out of the finest and thinnest wool, there will be more yards than in a pound spun from fibre of greater density and diameter. These numbers are based on yards per pound, and in the beginning—if not at the present—to describe wool as sixties implied that one pound of the combed top would give a uniform yarn of such fineness that sixty hanks, each of 560 yards, would go to the pound.

These numbers are the property of the worsted trade, which is that section of the manufacturing industry that is concerned with the longer wools. The shorter fleece wools, the shorter fibres of long-woolled fleeces, and the wool removed by the wool-comb (noils) are the raw material of the "clothing" or carded woollen trade. The distinction between short and long, like the distinction between merino and crossbred, marks another major division, and a more abiding one, running throughout the industry. The wool comb, a machine devised to select the longer fibres and to draw them parallel, has been so modified as to accept material shorter than did the combs of a few years ago, but there is a minimum limit to the length it can take. The carding industry, equipped with machines designed to intermix the longer and the shorter fibres, and to cause the former to carry the latter, has for its peculiar boast a saying that it can spin anything that is long enough to have two ends. The worsted industry is responsible for the suitings that bear its name for fine dress goods and linings. The woollen industry is the producer of tweeds, flannels, army, navy, police cloths, and blankets. The pair are intermarried in some directions, and tend to imitate each other and to overlap. Worsted imitates tweeds in some seasons, and tweeds repay the compliment in others. Worsted warps, or lengthwise threads, are used in fabrics made with woollen weft because the worsted thread is stronger. Woollen weft is used with worsted because it is cheaper, and weight is wanted in the cloth, or again because woollen does not polish and become shiny in wear, or because a more closely felted surface is required than can be got by use of the more wire-like worsted.

Despite their occasional correspondences, worsted and woollen remain distinct, using different material, different machinery and processes, and producing different classes of goods. The woollen industry is the consumer of the by-products of the worsted manufacture and the utiliser of the great reserve store of woollen material which exists in the form of rags. The one employing the long and the other the short wools, the two complete the economy of the industrial scheme. Worsted employs the more persons (116,649 in 1904), but of them a number are half-time workers, whereas the woollen trade with 98,800 persons finds little employment for those. Woollen manufacture is carried on in a larger number of premises. There are 1,377 woollen factories, and 841 worsted ones in the last available Home Office return—but there are special circumstances affecting these figures. In England the worsted industry tends to a strict sub-division of function.

The comber combs, the spinner spins, and the manufacturer weaves, quite commonly without carrying on any other considerable function. The woollen mills are more self-sufficing, the manufacturer is carder and spinner as well, and often dyer and cloth-finisher too. The worsted industry has a large foreign business in tops and yarn, which are not converted in this country into any kind of cloth. The woollen mills export but little in a half-finished state.

Limiting the case to fabrics and neglecting half-manufactured articles, it appears that woollen and worsted are near an equality. The Census of Production figures, when condensed, record an output in 1907 of £16,154,000 of fabrics of the worsted class, and of £18,933,000 of the woollen class. The statement omits carpets, which are properly products of a separate industry, and omits also certain minor articles including flannels and delaines, as belonging to both industries. In addition to the worsted cloth, the Census records the production separately of some £18,000,000 worth of worsted yarn, which amount is certainly much less than the truth. Up to 80,000,000 lbs. of worsted yarn, chiefly crossbred, and valued at over £8,000,000, is sent abroad in a year to feed looms working for the most part on the Continent. The Census figures are not final, and, because of anxiety to avoid duplication, are far from telling the whole tale, but they show a worsted and woollen output of £70,331,000. The exports of fabrics, yarns, tops, noils, and shoddy were 35,500,000 in the same year. One may be further wrong than in reckoning that the weaving mills work half for home and half for foreign orders.

Except of wool in the raw state, the import side is not very considerable in British experience. Imports of wool into this kingdom have reached lately a total of 800,000,000 lbs. a year, to which a home production of roughly 140,000,000 lbs. is to be added. Exports reduced the total available for home consumption to 612,000,000 lbs. in 1910, and 524,000,000 was the average retained in the quinquennium 1905-1909. To this is to be added skin wool, removed from woolled skins, and rag-wool, bringing the average total supplies during the five-year period to probably 752,000,000 lbs. a year, valued at £27,000,000. The gross value of imports of sheeps' and lambs' wool, mohair, alpaca, and vicuna has been in the same years £28,700,000 as an average and there has rested behind in this country £17,800,000 worth of imported raw material.

In other forms of wool, British exports largely exceed British imports. The 27,500,000 lbs. of worsted and woollen yarn, valued at £2,800,000 sterling, imported in 1910, was in excess of the recent average, but it does not bulk largely against the 94,000,000 lbs. valued at £9,000,000 sterling, exported in the same year. The import of wool fabrics is partly for re-export, and it has never been more than about £10,000,000 worth net, and was in 1910 under £6,000,000. The export of British woollen and worsted woven goods, exclusive of those shipped in the form of apparel, has been substantially £20,500,000 in 1905-09 and was over £25,000,000 in 1910.

The imports are of specialities, principally of goods which British manufacturers do not make, or are only beginning to make. The imported yarn is nearly all carded woollen, spun relatively fine, and used in this country in the weaving of shirtings, flannels, and dress goods and including some Berlin fingering, or knitting, wool. The fabrics are predominantly French dress goods made out of the South American wools which Englishmen, until recent times, preferred not to use, spun and combed on machines radically different from those most in use here. The type of cloth has been so closely imitated by Bradford manufacturers, that French competition is restricted principally to the lower and cheaper qualities of all-wool Amazon cloth and to articles of novelty. The German dress goods, of which a round million's worth per annum are imported, compete with French specialities and partly with English ones. The German cloths of heavier sorts owe their limited success in the English market to a fineness of face and a lustre that are due partly to the quality of the yarn and in part to the mode of finishing. The yarn is imported by English manufacturers and English machinists have improved on the German cloth-finishing machines.

The import of German cloth into England is some £300,000, or £1,500,000 sterling with dress goods, while the exports of British woollens and worsted to Germany are more. Germany is the principal export destination for English worsted yarns and tops, of which German manufacturers regularly consume some £6,000,000 worth a year.

The chief export destinations of British fabrics are found in the Empire. Canada in good years takes

By permission of] [*Messrs. Apperly Curtis & Co.*

WOOL AT THE MILL

£3,000,000 worth and Australia more than £2,000,000. Between one and two million's worth go to France and the United States, and over £2,000,000 worth to the southern Republics of South America, where the consumption of British woollen fabrics has undergone a wonderful expansion in ten years. Chile, Brazil, Argentina, and Uruguay have trebled their consumption of carded woollens in this short time. The markets change in importance under the influence of tariffs and the outlay of capital in new countries. One door opens when another closes, and there is the prospect of recovering in China more business than has been lost by the imposition of high duties in Japan.

Breeds of sheep and types of wool vary by districts, and are classified according to their locality, and the same is the case with mills and with their products. The cloths of one district are so nearly alike as to be clearly distinguishable from those of another, be it a very few miles away. The typical Bradford worsted coating may, with a moderate degree of expertitude, be recognised as different from the typical Huddersfield article. Batley woollens proclaim their difference from Morley and Guiseley or Colne Valley woollens at a glance. English worsted differs from Scotch worsted in appearance, and Yorkshire tweeds from Scotch and Irish ones in touch. Particular branches of industry tend to grow and develop in the same place, and generally in the same manner as that in which the branch was first introduced. The industry may be bodily transferred, as the worsted one was from Worsted in Norfolk to Bradford in Yorkshire, under stress of changes brought about by the introduction of steam and machinery. The face of the industry may be transformed as in Gloucestershire, the ancestral home of the manufacture of broadcloth. All industry is in a condition of flux and change, but the lineage of standard manufactures can still be traced through generations to particular district origins, and as the changes affect the surviving trades in a given district much in the same way, the family resemblances are retained and perpetuated. The effect of a century of steam and machinery has been to concentrate the British wool manufacture principally in England. Of the seventy and odd millions worth produced in 1907 over £63,500,000 are credited officially to England and Wales. Six millions worth, or less than one-tenth of the value, was produced by the mills of Scotland, and £607,000 by Irish mills. The manufacture has been concentrated in one part of England—Yorkshire, to wit, and further in one part of the West Riding of that county. Yorkshire claims roughly two-thirds of the mills, substantially all the rag-grinding machines, 90 per cent. of the wool combs, two-thirds of the spindles, four-fifths of the looms, and two-thirds of the workpeople. These are contained chiefly in a quadrilateral of which Haworth, Otley, Wakefield, and Holmfirth form the corners, and of which Bradford is the approximate centre. In Yorkshire the lowest and the highest meet. The most expensive worsted and the least expensive woollens, the finest dress goods and the coarsest stuffs, the most genuine of articles and the least blushing imitations, are produced at points almost within eyeshot of each other.

Outside Yorkshire, the tweed trade of the South of Scotland composes the largest group of mills. The mills number 53, have an output estimated at £3,000,000 in value, and engage some 12,500 persons. These are carded woollen mills, making the all-wool tweeds of which the whole world knows, and doing some worsted weaving. Worsteds were taken up in the dark days of the Scottish industry, and treated with the freedom and daring in design that has made tweed from the same source famous. These worsteds command high prices, and will probably continue to be produced despite the entrance upon a new lease of prosperity of the tweed trade. Shirtings and dress goods are woven near Glasgow, and isolated tweed mills exist in the Highlands. A thriving hosiery trade is springing up around Hawick, and Greenock has a flourishing worsted spinning and knitting mill. Ayrshire makes blankets, and Alloa knitting yarns are of the highest reputation, but the Border tweed trade comes first in the Scottish industry. The hand loom and spinning wheel remain in use in the Western Highlands and in Ireland, where their continued working is made possible by benevolent effort on the one hand and a sentimental preference on the other. The product is insignificant in amount, and distinguished by features which in mill productions are regarded as defects. The uneven yarn, the imperfections in weaving, crudity of colour and absence of finish, combine to give a distinctiveness of style for which there is a public willing to pay. Genuine homespuns are naturally superior to their own cheap imitations, but that they are in any respect better than cloths that can be made much more economically by machine is unproven. The idea that home-made goods demand more or higher skill and pains than power-woven ones is entertained most readily by those who know least of the labours of the mill and of the wealth of ability that is lavished on the manufacture of cloth.

The West of England, since the decay of business in the broadcloths of our grandfathers, has gone in a measure out of woollen manufacture. It continues to manufacture billiard, uniform, and overcoat cloth out of fine short wools in the traditional manner, and has added a business in worsted cloths to one in fancy tweeds. The Irish mills are woollen ones of growing reputation for fancy tweeds made from Irish and English Down wools, and for the national frieze. Wales continues in a relatively small way to make flannels and to deserve a good name for them. Rochdale is the chief base of the flannel trade, and elsewhere in Lancashire are produced worsted yarn and a variety of such undyed woollen goods as are used for mechanical purposes. Lancashire has, in the Rossendale Valley, a substantial monopoly of the manufacture of woollen felt. In Leicester worsted is spun for hosiery, and worsted has long been spun in Darlington. In Westmorland there is a limited production of saddler's woollen cloths. Cumberland produces tweeds, for caps and other purposes, at Carlisle. Devonshire makes serges at Buckfastleigh, and scattered about the counties are detached industries of smaller account. In sum, they do but emphasize the great accretion in and about the West Riding.

To answer why the West Riding has become the home centre of the trades would involve too large a draught of history and geography. Observe simply that worsted yarn was spun there before Bradford—on the breaking up of the East India Company's monopoly—succeeded in attracting to itself the weaving trade. Observe that the West Riding is near both coasts, has cheap fuel and large water supplies, and is where the iron and mechanical trades have developed also. Like other textile trades, the woollen and worsted ones provide abundant employment at tasks suited to women and children, and in the North of England there are many other industries to find husbands and fathers work. There were physical advantages, and there was a nucleus of workpeople with an understanding of the nature of wool and of the manual method of converting wool into yarn, and yarn into cloth. The combination has proved irresistible within its own scope, alike against other districts in this country and against the manufacturing genius of other countries. Nowhere are cheap tweeds made better at an equal price, and nowhere has the combing and spinning of strong and crossbred wools so prospered. The West Riding woollen and worsted industries are national specialities as well as local ones, as much as the Sheffield capacity for turning out steel, or Lyons for silk, Jena for glass, or Chemnitz for cotton hosiery.

The machines used in making British yarns and cloths are themselves British with only unimportant exceptions, and are made in the districts in which they are most in use. American ingenuity has appreciably improved on the older method of winding yarn, and an Englishman in American exile created the automatic loom which is tardily coming into the service of the worsted business. The Continent has furnished new ideas for the construction of machines for dyeing and finishing, but in general the machinery is English in conception, design, and build. The proximity of manufacturer and machinist is inestimably beneficial to both sides. The more he knows of industrial requirements the better the engineer can meet them. The manufacturer derives his benefit in prompt repairs and supply of spare parts, and in obtaining machinery at first hand and first cost, with none of the packing charges, railway carriage, ocean freight and duty which swell the cost of the same machines to many competitors abroad. It is officially reported, for example, that the machine which costs £100 to erect in an English mill costs £170 delivered at an American railway station. Textile machine making has been organised on a basis of cheap production and comparatively small profits, and from the consequent low prices the home manufacturer benefits more than anybody.

The machinists who equip the home mills equip also foreign ones. Bradford combs and Keighley spindles; Huddersfield cards and mules; Bradford, Keighley, and Huddersfield looms, work in all parts of the world, and in the home market makers of these prime machines have hardly one foreign competitor in sight. The export of machinery has been at various times spoken of as prejudicial to British manufacturing interests, but in affording employment for large numbers of men the export has the accompanying effect of liberating numbers of women for textile employment. Then, where British machinery is used abroad there is a demand for English managers and overlookers at good salaries. There is a connection less direct, but still perceptible, between use of British machines and demand for British supplies and materials. The owner of German carding engines buys German "specialities" of pulled waste and shoddy where the possessor of English machines buys from English sources. The order for machines is accompanied by orders for sundries running often to 30 per cent. of its total value. In the end, with the same machines, the same materials and imported English superintendence, it does not inevitably follow that the foreign user can produce identical results. In point of fact, he is often far from doing so.

Their quiverful of advantages gives British manufacturers a foremost place, but the industries employ more persons outside the Kingdom than within. Many as the English mills employ, the number of workers on their books is but a fraction of the total number of wage-earners in the wool manufacturing industry throughout the world. Over a quarter of a million persons in Germany, over 200,000 in France, about

163,000 in the United States, 150,000 in Russia, 80,000 in Italy, 53,000 in Austria, 35,000 or so in Belgium, 8,000 in Holland, 3,000 in India, and about 3,000 more employed in the woollen mills of Victoria and New Zealand, give basis enough for estimating that the world's total does not fall much short of 1,500,000 workers. Productiveness increases by dint of mechanical development without necessarily increasing the number of persons employed, and the British industry occupied substantially the same number in 1867 as in 1907, and in 1889 employed 40,000 more. Thus this estimate, based on returns taken at different dates, gives a clue to employment only, not to productivity.

CHAPTER III

WOOL AND ITS MARKETING

When wool is clipped from the sheep at shearing time, the individual fleeces rolled together and tied—in a proper order of things—with a loose twist made from their own fibre, are flung into a heap. The wool is packed by trampling into canvas bales and sent to auction sales or left in the heap to await the arrival of buyers. The statement outlines the practice in this country, but in Australia and New Zealand, where shearing and packing are done on a grander scale, more elaborate preparations are made for market. The Australian sheep is "dagged" two or three months before it is shorn, to save the blunting of shears at clipping time, and to spare the animal the necessity of carrying about pounds of matter interfering with the further growth of the fleece. In shearing, the belly-wool, which, by comparison, is short and tender, is severed first, the locks from the legs and elsewhere follow, and the rest comes off as one continuous fleece. The locks, pieces, and belly-wool are packed separately from each other, and the main body of the wool classed as "firsts" or "seconds," "clothing" or "combing," is packed separately and marked with the station brand and the wording denominating its quality. Largely because the wools are graded so carefully and honestly Australasian wool commands so ready a confidence and so good a price. The buyer has little fear of finding dirt and inferior wool in the heart of the bale, or secreted in the middle of the rolled fleece. Separated, each quality fetches its best price; miscellaneously mixed, so that nobody knows how much that is not wanted must be taken with that which is desired, wool does not realise its utmost value.

English wool is not classed regularly by the grower, although by all good farmers the fleece is "skirted" and the damaged portions are removed. The inclusion of inferior portions deceitfully is a kind of fraud probably less prevalent now than ever, but still not unknown. This, which is called "false winding," is a matter on which our forefathers were severe. A statute of Henry VIII declared that: "No person shall wind or cause to be wound in any fleece any wool not sufficiently rivered or washed, nor wind nor cause to be wound with any fleece clay, lead, stones, sand, tails, deceitful locks, cots, lamb's wool nor any other deceitful thing whereby the fleece may become weighty to the direct loss of the buyer." The "rivering," or washing of sheep, shortly before clipping time remains one of the distinctive sights of the English pastoral district. The sheepwasher, up to his middle in midstream, or standing outside the tank that also serves for disinfectant "dipping," seizes the swimming animal and souses it below the surface, rubbing vigorously with one hand to liberate the loose dirt in the fleece. A week or so later, and preferably before the yolk has had opportunity to rise again in the fleece, the shearing follows.

Clean, well-tended, and honestly packed though it be, the British farmers' wool is not necessarily in a condition to be bought advantageously by the consumer. Usually, the produce passes to a dealer's or stapler's hands to be further prepared by the removal of inferior portions or the putting together of similar fleeces or parts of fleeces. The wool is separated into "hogg" and "wether" accordingly as it is the first shorn or the product of a second shearing; or the fleece is broken up into "matching," that the consumer may have only the single quality he requires. There are differences in length and fineness in wool from the same sheep. The finest occurs on the shoulders, and the wool is progressively coarser the nearer it grows to the breech. The difference is immaterial for some purposes, and matters little to the woollen trade, but the penalty of mixing the sorts in worsted is found in unequal yarn and faulty cloth. It is after a number of handlings that the material is entrusted to the woolwashing machine. The machine is a succession of troughs, containing soap, alkali, and warm water, through which the wool travels on the teeth of swinging rakes.

The washing is followed by drying, done usually by a hot air-blast. The effect of the treatment is to clean the wool and make it appreciably lighter in weight. The loss of weight consequent on the abstraction of grease and dirt is variable. One hundred pounds of home grown Lincoln wool comes out weighing from 85 to 75 lbs., while the same gross weight of merino may yield as much as 50 or as little as 25 lbs. The figures throw a light on the difficulty of the woolbuyer's task. He has to judge the quality of the wool he sees and determine its general fitness for his work, which possibly presents no extreme difficulty.

To estimate within one or two per cent. what the net yield will be from a mass of wool, grease, seed, and sand, the unwashed produce of some hot, dry country, is a naturally different task. The buyer receives no encouragement to err by an average of more than 1 per cent., and there are in the trade a few hundred men, from England, Germany, France, and America principally, who can be trusted to buy wool upon the average within this narrow limit. They troop to Australia once a year to attend the round of auctions, and others of them assemble every two months or so in the Wool

Auction Room in Coleman Street. Their mornings are spent in the dock warehouses sampling the bales that have been sent there by the grower or the financial company that has advanced funds on the security of the wool. Their evenings are occupied in the sale room where wool is knocked down to the first giver of the highest bid by the presiding selling broker.

The greater part of the Australasian clip is sold by auction in the coast towns of Australia and New Zealand to buyers out from England, the Continent, the United States, and Japan. It is shipped in steamers to Europe at a cost of something like one halfpenny per pound of greasy wool in freight, and 7s. 6d. per £100 for insurance; or total charges of approximately £1 per bale. The clip was at one time sold almost entirely through London, and the respective claims of the rival markets are the constant theme of a sharp but not altogether edifying discussion. Whether in London or Australia, the lot is knocked down to the bidder of the highest price, whose bid is determined by the conditions prevailing in the market at the time. Those who sell in Australia sell soon, and those who consign to London sell later, and it is sometimes advantageous to sell, and at others to wait. Buyers certainly do not cross the world to pay more money than they need, and sellers do not give their selling-orders at home if they expect to realise better abroad. In some states of competition a larger selection of particular classes of wool is available in the Australian market, but this depends upon the policy of sellers for the time being. The London auctions clear about 1,000,000 bales a year, and the Colonial ones dispose of amounts ranging latterly from 1,300,000 to 2,000,000, and in favourable conditions some reselling of wool bought in Australasia occurs in London.

As well as colonial wool, quantities of foreign wool

By permission of] [*the British Australasian.*

ON A SHEEP FARM, AUSTRALIA

are sent to London, and the collection of foreign wools is at least catholic. It includes Bagdad, Bushire, Awassi, and Karadi wools; Syrian, Thibetan, Turkestan, Khorassan, Bokhara, Donskoi, Bessarabian and Calmuc sorts; East Indian, Pac Pathan, Joria, and Candahar wool; Madras wool; Ecuador, Peru, Lima, and Chili supplies; Turkish and Van mohair; China cashmeres; Syrian, Mongolian, Siberian, and Orenburg, Pekin and Tientsin camel hair; as well as wool from the River Plate, the Mediterranean, and Patagonia. Part of the Cape clip goes to Holland for sale, and Falkland wool goes to Liverpool as well as London.

The auctions in Australia follow in sequence in Sydney, Melbourne, Geelong, Adelaide, Brisbane, and Tasmania. The New Zealand ones begin at Wellington and are continued *seriatim* at Napier, Christchurch, Auckland, Dunedin, Timaru and Invercargill. The rotation is akin to that series of sales and fairs in which a large part of the English clip changes hands. The round begins at Leith in June, and ends in mid-September at Bristol. London remains the chief primary European market for Colonial wool, and Antwerp, aided by its water communication and contiguity to the French and German consuming centres, is chief for South American wools. Liverpool rivals London in the trade in low wools and receives the bulk of the clip of alpaca. Glasgow receives Cheviot and blackfaced wools, and, with Leith, is the depôt for Scotland. Bradford, the primary market for tops, is the depository market of a large part of the British clip, and of imported wool shipped there to be sorted for home and foreign consumption. On the Continent, Amsterdam, Havre, Hamburg, Bremen, and Marseilles are markets of importance, and Boston, Philadelphia, and New York the major wool trading centres in America.

In all the auctions the competition is by groups of men whose requirements are similar and known in advance. The bids of English consumers are principally for sound, clear lots embodying little waste, and topmakers or dealers buy to suit complex blends, and special opportunities of utilising lots of a more mixed character. German buyers present themselves in force especially to secure the finest merinos, the 70's, 80's, and 90's, which in actuality produce yarns finer than their nominal length. American buyers, with a careful eye for the artificial restrictions of the United States tariff, confine themselves to material on which there is a small scouring loss. The effect of this selection is seen in unequal demands for sorts of wool between which there is even only a small difference in quality.

Once out of the port-warehouse and on its way to the industrial centres, the wool has entered definitely upon its manufacturing career, and as much of it as is bought for English worsted purposes is sent to Bradford by rail and boat there to be sorted and blended with other wools for combing. The principal purchasers are the topmakers, who buy wool raw and sell wool combed, and shunt the noils down a side path. The topmaker's wool goes to his own or to a commission combing shed, and the tops pass eventually to a spinner, perhaps being dyed and recombed on the way. The spinner having converted the tops into yarn according to his orders from customers, the yarn proceeds to the manufacturer to be converted into cloth. The cloth goes to the dyer and finisher, and finally to the merchant, after it has been mended and freed from defects. The merchant in about half the cases is a shipper or supplier of merchants or importers abroad, who in turn are the fountain of supplies to smaller traders, by whom at length the manufactured article is put into stock. The merchant may be a home-trader, a supplier to tailors or drapers; or, again, the destination may not be a warehouse but a wholesale clothing factory. The list, if long, is not so complicated as the manufacturing path some wool pursues, and the transit of half the world made by the raw material is completed in more than a few instances by the transit of the other half by the finished goods.

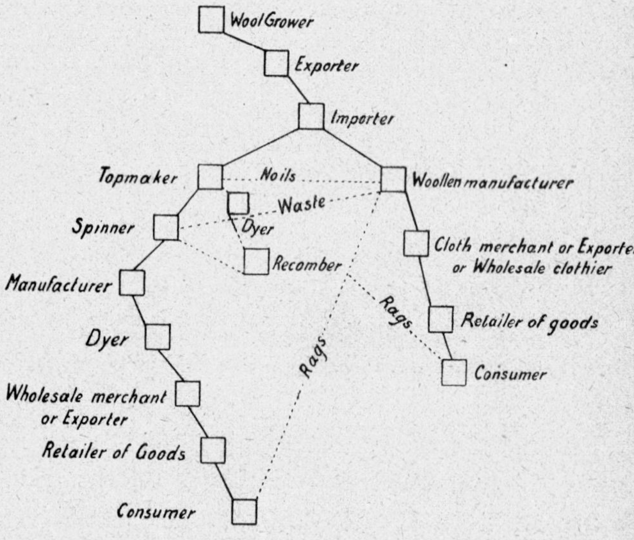

THE COURSE FOLLOWED BY WOOL IN ITS MANUFACTURE

The noils, it has been said, have been shunted down a separate path, usually into the hands of a dealer who deals also in the wastes or by-products created in spinning worsted. These are the natural food of the carded woollen trade, British or foreign, and go to make blankets or serges or tweeds, not improbably in conjunction with

A WOOL BARGE ON THE RIVER MURRAY, VICTORIA, TAKING WOOL TO THE SEA

that other recovered material known opprobriously as shoddy, and in the trade more usually referred to as waste. The course followed by woollen rags on their paths back to the mills is not less adventurous than that taken by virgin wool.

Collected from the clothing factory or tailor's shop, or from the housewife in exchange for crockery and toys, rags destined for remanufacture start on the tortuous course which leads to Dewsbury. There the rag auctions are held, and there, or near there, some 1,500 tons a week of home and foreign rags are reduced once more to spinnable fibre. The cast-off garment passes from the hawker to the small marine store dealer, who places it with garments of a similar kind. From his hands the rags go to those of a larger dealer, possibly in the capital or port, to be reclassified according to quality or colour, or to be torn apart at the seams to have the linings and pocketings removed. The dealer parts with them commonly to a shipper or merchant, to undergo further sorting and handling and reduction to a standard, to be packed and sent on consignment to the sales. There the bales are sold to the assembled buyers to be taken away and sorted more, to be dried and beaten free from dust by a machine, to be "seamed" by girls, or possibly to have the remnant of cotton removed by carbonisation in acid. Some of them are "stripped" or decolourised and dyed afresh. All that are fit for another period of service are passed through the "devil" or rag-pulling machine. The rags are nipped by rollers and shredded by revolving hardened steel teeth into their constituent fibres. The conversion of the waste articles, rags, into new, handsome, and serviceable cloth is not the least wonderful achievement of industry. There go to the work no less pains, skill, and taste than are employed in the production of other fabrics, and the ingenuity is, perhaps, greater than in making articles of more showiness from materials more promising in the inception. Certainly the operation arouses some jealousies. There are farmers who can never be persuaded that man ought to be allowed to make or wear cloth other than from new wool: and manufacturers who resent the competition of the cheap goods made from waste.

A host of misconceptions surround the word shoddy first of which is the notion that use of the material is unnecessary and even immoral. As to this it may be pointed out that the world wants warmth, and that the annual supply of virgin wool is limited. The supply is enough, upon Mr. Samuel S. Dale's calculation, to provide about 13 ounces of wool per head of the population outside the tropics; in short about enough to give each person as much cloth as would make a summer suit once in every five years. Wool, it is true, is weakened and shortened and deprived of some of its fine scales by its manufacture, remanufacture, and incidental washings and wear, but shoddy is not necessarily poor stuff. There are qualities of it as distinct as qualities among new wool, and it is undeniable that the best rag wool is superior in all respects to many wools that have not undergone a previous period of service.

Shoddy is strictly the name of long fibres recovered from knitted fabrics, or long-fibred and loosely compacted cloths. Mungo is the name for short fibre produced by grinding the harder cloths, but there is a place for short fibre as well as for long, and mungo is used not to the detriment of woollens, but for their improvement. With no mungo, there are handsome and durable milled cloths which could not be produced at all. And were the rag reserves, to the crying shame of the world, to be wasted, the upshot could only be that the many who could not pay for new wool must be clothed much worse. One had as well waste old metals as old wool; the consequences to the public at large would probably be less serious.

CHAPTER IV

COMBING AND SPINNING

In a reference already made to the scouring and drying done in preparing wool for the wool comb, nothing was said of the imperative necessity of soft water, pure soap, gentle alkali, and the avoidance of excess of heat whether in washing or drying. They are matters that cannot be overlooked by the man who is doing the work. Wool is easily injured in scouring, and the work is done very much better by some than others. It may be asked why not scour abroad, why pay freight on a bulk of greasy wool consisting half of impurity? The answer is that spinners do not wish their wool to be scoured except in the best manner, and in any case do not wish to have it press-packed and tight-bound for months after the operation. The excess freight is the less of two evils, and where the worsted user has his way the wool is not scoured at the point of production.

The wool is scoured at the combing-shed as part of the series of operations which turns wool into tops, and before combing the wool is opened preparatorily by one of two machines. The longer wools, exceeding seven inches in staple, are passed through the machines known as the "preparer gill boxes," into which wool is fed through rollers by means of travelling aprons. Within the box the wool fibres are stroked and humoured into a straight fore-and-aft position by travelling combs or "fallers." The latter are steel bars studded with steel pins on their upper surface, travelling faster than the wool, and propelled by a worm motion. At the end of its traverse each faller falls or sinks to the bottom of the box, is worked backwards to the starting point, and raised by the action of a cam to the upper screw. There is a succession of such "sheeter" boxes adjusted to perfect the ordering of the fibres and deliver the wool in a sheet or film. The sheet passes into other "boxes" designed to comb the wool further, draw the fibres lengthwise upon themselves and deliver not a sheet but a "sliver" or continuous untwisted rope of wool.

The alternative is to pass the wool through the worsted carding engine, and accordingly as the wool receives one or the other treatment its tops are known as "prepared" or "carded." The qualification denotes a difference in the length of the fibre used as well as difference of treatment. The carding engine is a machine of many cylinders, garnished with a myriad of fine wire teeth. There are main cylinders or "swifts" whose prime purpose is to carry the wool forward, and at different places, with different teeth and working at different speeds and in different directions, there are minor cylinders working upon the circumference of the swifts. The teeth tease and open the wool, and form it into a veil which is divided finally into slivers. Crushing rollers, or an arrangement of beaters, are set to remove so far as may be, the tenacious burr weeds gathered from the pastures. The preparatory treatment, the breaking of the burrs and of the nodules of dirt not removed entirely in the first scouring, involves in cases the necessity of backwashing. The name has a history dating from the time where the hand-comber had to take his tops back to the spinning factory and wash them there by hand before recombing them for final delivery. The modern backwasher is a mechanical contrivance of troughs of suds and mangle rollers for squeezing, with steam-heated drying cylinders behind. After backwashing comes the oiling of the wool.

By permission of] [*Messrs. Apperly Curtis & Co*

WOOL SCOURING

Scouring takes away much, and backwashing takes away more, of the fat natural to wool and, deprived of its grease, wool is at once more harsh and more brittle. The best olive oil is the chosen lubricant for diminishing breakage during the operation, as being that which is most readily and completely removable later, leaving the wool in the best condition in the end. Combing without oil is done upon wools intended for dyeing to light shades, where the least trace of discolouration is serious, but oil-combing is the rule, and is done on a scale which gives combers the liveliest interest in the olive-oil market.

The hand combers of two generations ago used oil and used heat, and the machine combers need both in combing. The hand comber combed by means of steel pins, and steel pins are still the means in use. The hand-worker used something like a rake furnished with long pins arranged in rows of descending length. A similar rake was attached to a post, and using a circular sweep the long fibres were gradually tickled away from one comb to another, and were worked from comb to comb in turn, the noil finally remaining near the roots of the teeth. The Noble comb, which is the type most in use to-day, works also with a circular motion, but the motion is horizontal not vertical, and the pins are short ones fixed in revolving circular plates. The wool is dabbed into teeth set upright in a large or main circle, and is worked upon by the pins set in the minor circles revolving upon the face of the larger and in the same direction. The long wool is drawn away by that circle which has gained the firmest hold, and formed into a fringe which is automatically drawn off, while the remnant of fibre too short to be caught up by the moving circles is left behind. The continuous taking-off forms the wool into a continuous twistless sliver, and the sliver is perfected by passage through a series of "finisher boxes" resembling the preparer boxes with which the process begins, but adjusted more closely. The machines are designed to blend and intermix the slivers thoroughly, and improve the uniformity of the top, finally turning off a finished sliver of which each yard has an equal and determined weight. The product is the "top" that is purchased by the spinner. Some idea of the economy of working may be got from the information that the cost of performing this long round of delicate and difficult operations involving the use of so much intricate and expensive machinery is—according to the class of wool—from 1⅛d. to 3¼d. a pound of finished top.

To become yarn fit for weaving or knitting, this top has to be attenuated more. The fibres have to be drawn over each other until the root of one is nearer to the top of another, and the whole has to be bound together by receiving twist. These are the operations performed by the worsted spinner who performs them gradually by successive steps nicely calculated to the determined end. The yarn, when finished, has to measure a definite number of yards to the pound, to be free from unduly thick or thin places, and have a certain uniform strength. It has to maintain the reputation of the spinner, give no cause for claims for damages on account of spoilt cloth, and still be produced continuously, steadily, and at astonishingly little expense. This result is unattainable without incessant attention to an infinitude of small details, and is arrived at by a close specialisation of function. A worsted spinner, except under circumstances of pressure, stands fast by his own qualities of material and his own range of "counts," finding his best chances of profit in the branch of business best known to him, and for which his machinery is most adapted.

When housewives spun with the aid of the hand-wheel, they divided their operation. First came the "drawing," done for the purpose of producing a loose and lightly-twisted cord of wool called "roving." Actual spinning followed when the roving was farther drawn by finger and thumb and twisted and wound upon a pirn. In worsted, this distinction between drawing and spinning persists, and the spinner goes to work to produce a perfect roving. The comber's top is "gilled" in machines differing only in fineness from the preparer and finisher boxes used in combing. After a suitable number of passages have been made by the fine steel pins the gilled tops with their fibres parallel and point-device, enter upon the drawing proper. The drawing boxes, like the preparer, finisher, and gilling boxes, have pairs of leather-covered rollers at each end, but are not furnished with teeth or "fallers." Inside are other rollers acting as carriers or supports.

The front and back rollers do the work, the front ones carrying the sliver in, and the back ones passing the sliver out. The back rollers are set to travel at a higher speed than those in front; they discharge sliver faster than it arrives, and draw the sliver finer by passing out a greater length than comes in. There is a sequence of these boxes, and in issuing from each of them the sliver is wound upon large bobbins and carried to the next. To ensure level drafting, the pull upon the fibres is never exerted twice consecutively in one direction. The front and back rollers are adjusted at such a distance apart that they should not break the longest fibres, and not leave the shorter ones unsupported for too great a while. The slivers are doubled and redoubled. At the first box six ends of sliver may be put in together and drawn into one, and in successive boxes 6, 5, 4, and 2 ends; which is to say, the material is doubled 5,760 times, and this is relatively a low number. Botany slivers are doubled in this cumulative way hundreds of thousands of times, to secure a perfect uniformity of mixture and hence an equal yarn of whatever fineness capable of producing a faultlessly even and unbroken surface upon the face of the cloth.

Spinning is only the completion of a work that has been three-parts done. It rests to draw or draft the roving still finer, put in more twist and wind up the spun thread in some convenient form. The further drafting is done again by rollers set to exercise drag upon the passing roving, and these are the first working parts of all spinning frames. The second essential is the arrangement for twisting, which is not the same in all frames. Three types of frames are used in worsted—the flyer, cap, and ring.

The flyer frame is useful for thick counts and all qualities, and for producing a smooth yarn free from "beard" or surface hairs, but it cannot be run at so high a speed as the cap spindle. The ring frame is used more commonly in doubling than spinning. A pair of arms rotating round the bobbin give the flyer frame its name, and these move faster than the bobbin itself, carrying the yarn in an eye at the lower extremity of one arm. The bobbin winds, and the flyer puts in the twist, giving in accordance with its speed and that of the bobbin a regulated number of turns per inch. The less the twist and the greater the off-turn.

Cap-spinning frames are used for Botany, and are unsuitable for rebellious material, and in them the spindles do not revolve. Motion is given to the bobbin by a tube around which the bobbin fits. The cap of steel, a little larger than the head of the bobbin, rests stationary upon the spindle head, serving as a guide to the yarn and providing a relatively frictionless surface. The bobbin revolves inside the cap, and the number of revolutions it makes during the period of time in which the delivery rollers turn off one inch determines the number of turns per inch (*i.e.*, the amount of twist) in the yarn.

In the ring frame spindle and bobbin revolve, and a light drag is put upon the thread by a ring of bent wire known as the "traveller," which is drawn round the flange of an annular opening in a rail. The opening in the rail surrounds the bobbin, and a gentle up and down motion imparted to the rail, guides and equally distributes the yarn over the bobbin's whole length.

There are important differences in the speeds at which the several kinds of frames can be run, and this affects the production. At a speed higher than 2,500 revolutions a minute, the vibration in flyer-spinning is injurious to the yarn, but the flyer is used in general for all counts up to 24's. The cap frame driven at nearly three times the speed, or the ring frame, are used for yarns of greater fineness.

The spinning frame produces "singles" (yarn of a single strand) but the greater part of worsted is sold two-fold. The doubling is effected on a machine differing from the spinning frame in being without drafting rollers. The yarn leaves the spinner's hands after being wound into the form required, and the machinery used in rewinding from the spinning bobbins has been the subject of new attention and ingenuity. The outsider is most familiar with yarn in hanks or skeins, but to meet varying trade needs, yarn is wound conically on tubes or is crossed and recrossed on other tubes into the shape known expressively as "cheeses." Again, it is wound into bottle-shape upon bobbins, but for weaving purposes its principal appearance is in one of two forms: on spools for use as weft, and on beams for use as warp. The beam is a giant bobbin the width of the loom, and the threads to form the warp of the cloth are wound parallel upon it in the machine known as the warping-mill in such number and length as are required.

Reference has been made to the cheapness with which yarns can be drawn and spun from tops. The cost when done by a commission-spinner who takes no responsibility for the waste created, is about 3d. per lb. of 2/24's, 4½d. per lb. of 2/40's, or 9d. per lb. of 2/60's. The numbers denote the "counts" of yarn, in other words, the number of hanks of 560 yards in 1 lb. In single 60's yarn there are 33,600 yards per lb., and in 2/60's two single threads of this count are twisted giving a finished length of 16,800 yards, or approximately nine and a half miles.

Exactness of count is reached with marvellously little deviation, and in the yarn contract rules made by the Bradford Chamber of Commerce there is provided a margin of not more than 1 per cent. This allowance is made not to cover error, but as a provision against the shrinkage to which yarns, like cloth, are liable. Shrinkage apart, it is required that hanks drawn from a bundle shall average 560 yards per lb. This exactitude in the matter of length in conjunction with the undeviating regularity in point of diameter, is the best evidence of the delicacy and care requisite in worsted spinning.

CHAPTER V

CARDS AND MULES

WORSTED begins by rejecting the short fibres and selecting from the long those that are most uniform in length and diameter. Worsted processes aim sedulously at preserving the parallelism of the constituent filaments, and this feature the woollen processes consistently avoid. The woollen manufacturer's aim is the production of a yarn in which the fibres are mixed at all angles and in which the longer hold and support the short. There is no combing and all the stroking and teasing out is done with a different aim.

The raw material is opened by means gentle or severe according to its nature or state, and whether the opening out is preceded by scouring or dyeing depends on what the material is. The typical opening machine is the "willey," in which a cylinder of three or four feet diameter, garnished with steel hooks, carries the material round to be operated upon by three cylinders furnished similarly and working in the opposing direction. The willey in its main lines is typical of the machines which follow it and have supplanted the flat hand-cards of the housewife. These instruments, shaped like fire-shovels or curry combs, were bristled with pins of spring wire set in a foundation of leather and were manipulated like hand brushes to work the material into a spongy pad from which a sliver reducible upon the spinning wheel to a continuous roving was drawn by hand. The teeth remain but are mounted on rollers and not upon flats. The hooks of the willey are succeeded in the carding machines by a card-clothing of pins, graduated

By permission of] [*Messrs. William Lupton & Co.*

IN THE WILLEY HOUSE

in fineness and sharpness according to the work they have to do, and adjusted to turn out continuously a smooth and regular supply of sliver.

The material, after being oiled and blended, passes to the carding-engines, of which three are used; the first, or "scribbler," being for the rougher work. Wool, weighed out by an automatic device for securing a regular even feeding, is received on a feed-apron and taken up by the "licker-in." The wool is removed by a neighbouring roller and delivered to the fast-moving main cylinder or "swift." The wool travels into the slow-moving teeth of a "worker" roller turning in the opposite direction, is stripped and passed to another worker roller and back to the swift. The wool is lifted lightly from the pins of the main cylinder by the intersecting pins of the "fancy" and is finally cleared by a "doffer" and passes on to a second, third, or fourth swift.

The "scribbler" feeds the "intermediate" card, and carding is finished and a continuous sliver is formed by the third engine or "condenser." The woollen objective is the production of yarn with fibres lying within it at all angles, but the card teeth tend to draw the fibres straight. To defeat this effect, in passing from one card to the next, the fibres are delivered to the succeeding machine in a direction at right-angles to that in which they came out of the last. In the end there is a close and delicate veil of wool nearly two yards wide resting on the teeth of the final card and awaiting division and condensing. This completed, the sliver is ready for the mule.

The spinning mule with its round of complex motions is the most fascinating of machines to watch. More exactly than the worsted-spinning frames, it reproduces the motions of the spinster at the hand wheel. She

Wool

Sorting table

Scouring machine & drying

Preparing

Combing

Drawing

Spinning

Winding & Warping

Weaving

Dyeing & Finishing

Piece-dyed Worsted Cloth

Noils

Waste

Opening

Blending & Oiling

Willeying

Carding & Condensing

Mule-spinning

Winding & Warping

Weaving

Dyeing & Finishing

Piece-dyed Woollen Cloth

THE ORDER AND SUCCESSION OF THE MANUFACTURING PROCESSES

attenuated her thread by drawing away her hand from the spindle. In the mule the condensed sliver is drawn thinner by the outward motion of a carriage bearing the spindles which retreats bodily on wheels and rails away from the rollers that pay out the sliver. Automatically, the spindles by revolving apply a slight twist during the outward run and automatically the supply of sliver stops. The carriage continues the outward run and the spindles continue to put in twist. The carriage stops, the spindles double their speed to put in more twist, and the carriage moves homewards a little way. The twisting stops, the mule backs off and returns a few inches, a taut wire comes into action to maintain the tension on the 400 threads. The carriage completes its return home to the face of the rollers with the 400 spindles energetically winding up the yarn that has been drawn and spun during the operation.

The outcome of the woollen operation is a yarn inferior in tensile strength to the product of the worsted process but greatly superior in felting properties. The fibres crossing and recrossing in the yarn, are in the positions in which the minute serrations, discoverable with a microscope upon the edges of all wools, are best able to interlock—as they are made to do in cloth finishing. The yarn is softer and bulkier than worsted and capable of undergoing greater changes and hence of producing a greater variety of effects in cloth.

Yarn is not, on the whole, produced from wool more cheaply by card and mule than by comb and frame, but it may be made of cheaper materials and hence be cheaper in the end. The worsted spinner is tied to new wool and long wool; the woollen spinner is free to suit his purposes by mixture of woollen wastes and cotton. Worsted yarn fluctuates in price in sympathy with the wool and top market. By reason of the wider

By permission of] [*Messrs. William Lupton & Co.*

SPINNING MULE AT WORK

choice of materials prices of woollen yarn change relatively seldom. And this fıeedom of choice, introducing greater possibilities of complexity, brings also more opportunities for the exercise of skill.

More than a little ingenuity is used in compounding a serviceable worsted top for the market and bringing it in at a low price. The topmaker considers length, softness, colour, and all that goes to make the characteristic described vaguely as quality. He intermixes fleece wools from different sources according to their suitability and price, and possibly adds skin wool and odds and ends, but his freedom is short in contrast with that of the woollen carder. In blending and carding woollens profits are lost or made. The blend determines the price and the output from the cards governs the production of the whole of the rest of the mill. The successful carder exhibits his skill in "getting weight back," which is to say avoiding loss of material in working; by putting through a maximum quantity of wool per day and producing at the same time a homogeneous mixture from which the spinner can turn out a yarn even in thickness and uniform in strength. The number of the carding machines is the measure of the woollen mill, and in comparing sizes of mills it is customary to count not looms or spindles but "sets"—sets of cards with their appurtenants.

CHAPTER VI

CLOTH MAKING

KNITTING has enormously developed, partly at the expense of woven goods. The knitted undergarment has replaced the flannel one, and when the season turns it is the knitted garments rather than the woven ones that are changed. Withal weaving is the main outlet for worsted and woollen yarn, and the loom in its main essentials is the same in principle as that which Eastern craftsmen have improvised from time immemorial with a few sticks and an end or two of rope. A means of holding the warp and of parting its threads, a means of throwing the weft across the "shed" formed when the warp threads are lifted, and a means of beating up the weft when woven, are the features of all looms of all times.

Hand looms for woollens were common up to fifty years ago in England, where the hand loom only survives as an instrument for weaving pattern lengths in the mill and as a domestic machine in cottage industry. The power loom differs from it in speed and complexity. The manual weaver lifts the "healds" controlling the warp threads by levers operated by foot and throws the shuttle by use of a strap and arm worked by hand, beating home the threads when woven by reed wires. The power loom is heavier and fitted with more motions than could conveniently be worked by foot and hand. Its parts are more completely controlled and their functioning is more regular. The warp is let off automatically from its beam, the cloth is automatically taken up as it is woven, the shedding answers obediently to an arrangement of pegs set in holes, and the throwing of the shuttle to form the pattern, and the beating up of the weft are done by power. The weaver's work is largely watching and putting in fresh supplies of weft. Even the replenishing of shuttles is automatic on certain looms and by a delicate attachment the whole apparatus is brought to a standstill on the breaking of a thread.

The woollen loom used for the production of heavy cloths out of yarn not able to take much strain run slowly, making from 40 to 60 " picks " or passages of weft per minute on the obsolescent type of machine. The worsted broad loom runs faster, say at 90 to 100 picks, the fast coating loom at 100 to 140, and the narrow dress goods loom fastest of all at the rate of 200 picks a minute. The production of cloth on any loom varies with the speed and with the picks per inch. In a heavy woollen with coarse yarn the weft threads in one inch may number no more than thirty, and in a fine worsted be as many as 200. Seventy yards of one fabric take one day to weave, while the same length of a different one will take a week. One weaver looks after two looms weaving the plainer and simpler goods, but one weaver to one loom is the rule where the highest classes of fabric are produced. Differences so important have equally important effects on the cost of weaving and prevent the making of any useful generalisation.

Various other considerations affect the economy of weaving. To begin with, the warp has to be dressed free from its imperfections, and each " end " of the warp according to its place in the design has to be tied into the loom individually. The cost of the latter work is as great for a short warp as a long one and during the time that the twisting-in is being done the loom is at a standstill. Then high speed in weaving has compensating disadvantages. The faster the weaving and the more

By kind permission of] [*Messrs. Priestley, Ltd.*

SECTION OF A WEAVING SHED

necessity there arises for subsequent mending when, with needle and short length of yarn, the girl mender remedies the deficiencies left by the loom. Mending and burling cost as much as weaving in the production of certain goods, and sometimes very much more. The mender replaces missing threads and repairs damages so far as is practicable. The burler removes with tweezers the stray filaments of foreign fibres such as have refused in the dye bath to accept the same dye as the wool. Strips of weed gathered in the pastures, or fibres of jute rubbed from the inside of woolbags become incorporated with the wool and pass through the processes without detection to appear as expensive blemishes at last on the face of a fine worsted fabric.

Cloth, as it leaves the loom, is short of at least half the attractions that cloth has in wear. It is open in texture, redolent of oil, and even if dyed in the yarn or wool is duller in appearance than finished cloth. Wool is dyed in any of four stages. Loose scoured wool is dyed for the use of the carded woollen manufacturers. Worsted tops or "slubbing" is dyed for the spinner of mixture coloured worsted yarn. Yarn is dyed for fancy cloths either in warp form or in hanks. More is dyed after weaving and the cloth is described then as piece-dyed. Cloth undyed is "in the grey" and the sight of it gives little enough idea of what dyer and finisher between them will make of it. The woollen manufacturer usually finishes, although he does not always dye, his own fabrics, for woollens in especial are plastic enough to be made or marred in finishing. The worsted manufacturer delegates both functions ordinarily to a commission dyer and finisher who carries on the process on a relatively large scale.

The routine of piece-dyeing and finishing varies in its broader details with the circumstances, and in its smaller details varies in accordance with the result required. First, the grey cloth is relieved of the oil used by the comber or carder and this is done in laundry fashion. Pieces stitched head to tail, forming a band perhaps some hundreds of yards long, are run through a warm soap solution in the " dolly." From the trough of suds the cloth is passed and repassed through massive wooden and squeezing rollers for as long as two or three hours. " Milling " follows, an operation once performed by the feet and later by the fulling " stocks." The process aims at felting together the loose structure formed in the loom, and woollens are made with a view to a close condensation at this stage. The fabric gains in substance what it loses in width and length and the treatment may be of any severity. In the fulling stocks ponderous mallet heads, actuated like trip hammers, are raised and left to fall alternately upon the cloth as it lies in a lump in a trough or basin. With every blow the cloth is moved a little and all parts of it in turn are hammered equally. Rollers replace the hammer in the milling machine and reduce the cloth in width while compression in a funnel-shaped passage contracts the cloth in length. Heat, alkali, and pressure in combination cause wool to shrink and all three factors are present. The minute scales or serrations lock and interlock, the fibres creep together more closely, and in woollens the fibres are felted and matted. In worsted, where the opportunity of felting is less, the fibres burst loose by the treatment appear on the surface and form a loose nap or " cover " upon the face.

Wool dyeing is done with boiling water and before the fabric can safely be sent to the dyeing machine it must be " set " to prevent an unequal shrinkage that might cause crimped or cockled patches. The operation is called " crabbing " and is done on a relatively simple machine. The cloth is wound carefully at full-width upon a roller and led through troughs of hot water and cold alternately to a further roller, hollow and perforated, on which the cloth is rewound and boiled or steamed. Dyeing follows in a vessel heated by steam-jets and fitted with rollers against which the cloth runs. The detail varies with the dyestuffs used and various of them require more than one operation to dye and fix the colour upon the fibre. Dyeing is followed by washing to remove loose colour, and by tentering to preserve the width of the cloth. The lists or edges are brushed down upon parallel rows of pins set in the " tentering " machine at a distance apart equal to the width the cloth is to have when finished. The fabric is " dewed " or moistened to restore the moisture proper to its nature. Its surface is raised or scratched, if need be, either with a drum set with teazles imported from France for the purpose or with steel pins set on rollers. These thistle heads or wires raise a pile upon the surface which the cutting-machine reduces or removes. The cutting blades are set spirally as in a lawn mower and are adjustable delicately to the work. The finishing ends ordinarily with pressing. The cloth, thrown into equal folds, plaits, or " cuttles " by machine is interleaved with cardboard presspapers. Hot and heavy iron plates from a steam-oven are placed between each piece in the upright pile in which the goods are stacked in a hydraulic press. The pressure is applied and maintained for a time and at a power proportionate to the effect sought or the kind of goods treated.

Pressing consolidates and smartens the appearance of the cloth, giving it in some circumstances more glaze than is required. The removal of this surplus finish, and the reduction of the cloth to a state in which it will not shrink in wear, is the function of the " London shrinker."

By permission of] [*Messrs. Apperly Curtis & Co.*

CLOTH-FINISHING

The cloth is wetted by the shrinker between moist layers of canvas and hung up to dry, or it is mechanically wetted and dried without heat.

An alternative to London-shrinking is applied as the final operation to large quantities of cloth. The fabric is rainproofed by a process which, while leaving the cloth porous, improves its resistance to wet. The regular method involves two steps. The cloth is impregnated thoroughly with a solution of acetate of alumina, a chemical highly soluble in water and so not in itself a sufficient protection against rain. In course of drying, or after drying, the cloth is coated with a fine film of hard wax, applied either in a melted state or by dry friction. The wax, in addition to acting as a waterproofing substance on its own account, assists to lock the soluble acetate within the fibre. The process is very much cheaper than the system of waterproofing by means of rubber. It is effected in one passage through a continuous machine and is completed by pressing the goods to restore the required degree of finish.

If the means employed in cloth-finishing seem simple the effects produced are strikingly complex. The changes wrought in what might excusably be taken for a soiled sail-cloth in the first instance are conspicuous to the eye, but the finisher has to satisfy another of the senses. The "handle" of the goods must be neither too sharp nor too soft. The weight per running yard must be right and there has to be neither too much nor too little nap or cover. The design of the cloth has not to be over-distinct nor yet too much broken, and between wrong and right, between what any bungler can do and the complete cloth finisher can do with the same means and material, there is a gulf wider than might be believed. In truth, the work calls for the nicest apprehension and the most delicate judgment. The whole matter is one of hairbreadths, and by signs incomprehensible to the layman, the practised finisher brings the cycle of processes to a perfect culmination.

The processes employed in bringing, for example, mohair and worsted and cotton linings to the full height of their lustre are destructively severe. The finishing treatment designed to add to their appearance is at the expense of strength of the goods. Improvements in obtaining not merely lustre, but permanence of lustre, come as the outcome of bold experiments involving often the ruin of hundreds of pounds worth of goods. Any marked failing in the finished result is visited by penalties that are always heavy. The goods if declined by the original customer may go a-begging in vain. If they have to be sold as "jobs" for the account of the dyer and finisher who has spoilt them, he is fortunate indeed to escape with a loss of not more than fifty per cent.

CHAPTER VII

THE NATURE OF CLOTH

As it presents itself to the practical manufacturer a given cloth represents, firstly, wool of a certain quality, yarn of a certain count, woven with a certain number of threads per inch and finished in a particular manner. The quality betrays itself at once to the experienced touch and the count of yarn can be inferred, judged by comparative test or ascertained with more certainty by delicate weighing. The weft and warp threads can be counted and there results a statement of particulars of which this is an example bearing on a light worsted fabric :—

Warp.	Ends.	Sett.	Picks.	Weft.
2|32s	3002	52	56	1/24s

70 yds. warp, 63 yds. finished.
64 ins. wide, 58 ins. finished, 10-10½ oz. per yd.

The weight of the warp is found by multiplying the ends (3002) by the length (70) which gives as the product the total number of yards ; this divided by the hanks per lb. (16 = ½ of 32) multiplied by the yards per hank (560) gives the weight of approximately 23½ lbs. per piece. The weight of weft is the balance required to make up the weight of the cloth in the grey state, from which an allowance of five per cent. or so is to be allowed for loss in waste and shrinkage. The prices of the yarns being known, the cost of weaving being taken at the price paid in the district, and costs of dyeing, mending, and finishing added, the net cost of manufacture is obtained. The cost of all processes incidental to weaving is reckoned in the district from which the sample in question comes at double the amount paid in wages to the weaver.

A hundred incidental considerations affect the value at any particular moment of any given sample of cloth. The price of raw material, the amount of stock on hand, the fashion in colour and design, or the season of year, will influence buyers in one direction or another. In the market sense cloth is worth what it will fetch, and in practice cloth to realise to the best purpose has to conform to the arbitrary limits which custom and competition set. It has to display certain superficial attractions, possess some solid qualities, and withstand comparison with any goods that might be used in its stead. No close familiarity with the operations of manufacturing is necessary in order to make a shrewd guess at the actual worth of a fabric. Were it otherwise, buyers would be less successful in beating sellers down. What is essential is that one should have certain powers of observation and a familiarity with the prices and characteristics of cloths of a similar kind.

The permanent features which lend value to cloth begin with the raw material of which it is made. The fineness of the yarn from which it is woven and the number of threads to the inch are other considerations of the same class. Some idea, however rough, can be gained by making a dissection, releasing and unravelling bits of yarn to judge of the length and fineness of the fibres and to see whether the thread is single or two-fold. There are tests which can be applied hastily to determine of what the material is made. If there is doubt whether a particular thread is wool at all, something is to be learnt by biting it. Wool is characteristically harsh and gritty between the teeth and the differences of sensation can readily be proved by experiment, choosing one known wool and one known cotton thread. Silk cuts when bitten and cotton crushes between the teeth. Wool is readily distinguished from cotton by burning. A cotton thread carries the flame, burning freely, where a woollen or worsted thread chars, swells, refuses to carry the flame, and emits a smell of burning horn. A woollen thread is distinguishable from a worsted one by noting the direction of the fibres either with the naked eye or through a magnifying glass, observing whether they are parallel or not.

For counting picks the folding glass known as the piece glass, fitted above with a lens and below with a measured slit in the metal is useful, although a more elaborate and accurate instrument can be had. The threads in one-quarter, half, or whole inch are counted in the lighter worsteds, and in such goods as linings the number of threads forms the only guide to small differences of quality, inappreciable to the eye or touch. Quality of material and size of yarns being the same, that sample which has the more threads is the better. In heavier goods the index is weight rather than number of threads, and values are shaped—other things equal—by the ounces per yard or pounds per piece. Width is a consideration for the study of those who expect economy in cutting cloth for garments. Strength is a factor making for success in wear, and the Government Departments, for example, use machines for testing the elasticity and tensile strength of the woollens they buy. A sample of determined size is held between jaws and a measured strain is applied. The stretch is noted and the breaking point. The result is more exact than that obtained in the customary way by applying the thumb test. In this rough and ready test the fingers are closed, the knuckles laid in face of each other and the cloth is held firmly between the clenched forefingers and the extended thumbs. Force is used, keeping the thumbs together and the ease or difficulty experienced in bursting a hole in the fabric by downward straining give a clue to the suitability of the cloth to resist strains.

The tests with a flame or with the teeth are not ineffective where the yarn tested is all cotton or all wool. They suffice for rough purposes also in cases where a thread of wool is twisted with one of cotton to make twofold yarn. When the cotton is "scribbled" into woollen, and indistinguishable by the eye or touch, these tests fail to tell anything conclusive. A more elaborate means is taken of proving the existence of cotton in this form, but the proof is still easy. The sample is boiled in a caustic soda solution made strong enough to dissolve the wool. The cotton remains and by washing, drying, and weighing the residue its proportion to the whole may be established. Cotton is an illicit ingredient in goods described as "all wool," but it is not the case that the presence of cotton is always a disadvantage. A proportion of cotton, sufficient to lend strength, makes an otherwise "tender" woollen of more value from all points of view. Cotton, in the cheap woollens of the day, plays the same part as steel girders in an otherwise unsafe building, bracing and supporting the whole.

An alternate means of detecting cotton lies in dyeing the fabric with one of the colours which will only colour wool. Cotton does not take the same dyes and advantage is taken of the fact in designing goods. The wool is dyed and the cotton in refusing the colour leaves a parti-coloured effect. The so-called union goods, which have a warp entirely of cotton, have an excuse apart from either cheapness or strength. Cotton lies in little room and is eminently pliable, and use of it, along with the more bulky worsted, produces results not obtainable by using only wool. Manufacturing is utilitarian or nothing, and no one is to be blamed for turning whatever material is to be had to the best use. The grievance, if any, is one of misrepresentation, and woollen manufacturers are too little in contact with the non-technical public to be very guilty in that respect.

The invention of the sewing machine, and the consequent cheapening of the process of converting cloth into clothes, accounts in large measure for the comparative disregard shown to the wearing qualities of wool goods. When cloth itself was dearer, owing to the backward state of mechanical invention, when general wages were lower and garments were made singly by hand, a new suit or a new dress was a rarity of some value. The disappointment was profound if the clothes failed to wear well and look well for a much greater length of time than one expects to wear a modern cheap suit. Fashion changed less suddenly or fashionable decrees were unheeded by a greater proportion of people in our grandfather's days. With the cheapening of manufacture and of making-up, the increase in general spending power, and the growth of Jack's desire to look as well as his master, has arisen a fondness for change of clothing. Clothes are bought more for their looks and low price and less for their solid qualities and real economy. They are not built to outwear their popularity and rather than have one good suit or dress, two different ones at the same cost are preferred by the majority of consumers. The inclination is one that manufacturers have an incentive to encourage.

Clothes not only as good, but better than ever, are made nowadays, but it is rather upon outward looks than on inward worth that ingenuity expends itself. Wearers of the most expensive cloths are the least exacting in the demand for durability, and buyers of the cheapest know that wearing power is not a thing they have paid for and can expect. The finest fancy worsteds by the most reputed makers fetch fifty per cent. more than worsteds, not materially unlike them, but made in larger bulk for a different class of people by less renowned manufacturers. The difference is explained by the display of a faultlessly classic taste in design and colour, a flawless perfection of weaving and finishing, the excess cost of manufacturing small lots instead of large ones, and the extremely heavy cost of preparing and selecting patterns to please the most fastidious fancy. More than one Huddersfield worsted mill spends in patterns and designing over £15,000 per annum, and in any of the tweed and worsted mills of the highest class the cost runs into thousands annually. The expenditure is not primarily directed to making cloth that will wear. Cloth that will sell and not belie the wearer's expectation is the aim in these mills as in other ones.

Trade necessities rigorously enforce the maintenance of a standard of strength as of other qualities. Cloths disappointing in wear come back to the mill in garment form and claims for damages come with them. The wholesaler rejects goods visibly below standard and a small defect is the source of a disproportionately heavy loss. There is no lack of pains to see that cloths are strong and well-balanced and their colours fast. A minimum requirement is imposed on all goods intended for the market and everything else is relative to price and purpose.

Makers of expensive cloths test the colours that they use by exposing samples to twelve months' sun and rain and judge of their fastness to light accordingly. The resistance of coloured dress goods to street mud is tried by sprinkling a sample with lime and water and brushing off the incrustation when dry. The common standard of the fastness of navy blue for serge is to boil a pattern in a solution of washing soda of the strength of one ounce to one quart. Apart from the wet tests and testing by sunlight is the test for fastness in rubbing. A screw of white paper, or an unstarched white handkerchief, rubbed on the surface of the cloth supplies evidence promptly of whether the dye is loose. The "crocking" or rubbing off of colour is a weak point, but it is a defect inseparable from use of indigo. Piece-dyed indigo blue rubs off a little, yarn-dyed indigo more, and wool-dyed indigo most of all. The more the "crocking" in general the better the indigo.

The permanence of finishes is also susceptible of test. The most trying is to lay the sample upon a moist pad and lay upon it a hot iron. The general standard of fastness of finish in such goods as worsted linings is to immerse half a sample of cloth in boiling water until it is thoroughly wetted through and then to allow the sample to dry naturally. The wetted half is compared with that which has not been treated.

Rule-of-thumb tests are supplemented by more exact and scientific observations taken with the assistance of such apparatus as the consultants, chemists, and testing houses attached to the industry have at elbow. Fine tests are indispensable to detect small differences and are necessitated by causes of dispute, but a great deal of business is done purely on the evidence of the most elementary safeguards.

CHAPTER VIII

TEXTILE TESTING-HOUSES AND TECHNICAL SCHOOLS

THE requirements more especially of international trade have called into being such conditioning-houses as that at Bradford. Conditioning houses are the assay-offices of textile industry and are most used where the most expensive textile materials are handled. The silk trade is supplied with conditioning-houses in all the Continental centres and the bulk of silk used is "conditioned" in them. There are evident reasons why establishments of the same sort should be necessary where wool is handled in bulk. It is not uncommon for spinners to order at one time 1,000 packs (240,000 lbs.) of tops worth, perhaps, £30,000. So little as one half per cent. of surplus moisture means on this quantity £150 and the initial purpose of a conditioning-house is to ensure that in paying for wool one is not buying water.

Wool is by nature hygroscopic and varying with its kind and state takes up different proportions of atmospheric moisture. It is against the interest of sellers to send in wool too dry and against that of buyers to pay for material too damp. Accordingly standards of moisture have been arranged and to determine whether wool material is above or below standard it is sent into the conditioning-house, which, in Bradford, is a profit-making municipal institution controlled by a joint committee of the municipality and of traders. Samples are drawn from different parts of the bale and the representative sample thus obtained is reduced to a condition of absolute dryness. The sample is lowered

6—(1459)

in a wire cage into the inside of a specially designed gas-oven and dried by an ascending column of hot air. The cage hangs upon one arm of a beam-scale and the gradual loss of weight as the drying proceeds is noted. When the loss has ceased and a condition of bone-dryness exists, the dry weight is recorded and the original weight is compared with that obtained by adding to the dry-weight the conventional "regain." On the result of the tests a certificate is issued showing the variation from the standard weight. Regains are allowed as follows :—

Wool and waste ..	16	per cent.
Tops combed in oil ..	19	,, ,,
Tops combed without oil	18¼	,, ,,
Ordinary noils	14	,, ,,
Clean noils	16	,, ,,
Worsted yarns	18¼	,, ,,
Woollen and worsted cloth	16	,, ,,

The regain is not identical with contents of water with which it is sometimes confused. One hundred pounds of absolutely dry tops become 119 lbs. with regain and the content of moisture is 19 in 119 and not in 100; thus the normal content is 15·96 per cent. in the case of oil-combed tops.

Wool materials lose or gain weight according to the temperature and humidity of the surroundings in which they are stored and the conditioning-houses certify what the condition was at the time of delivery, so avoiding dispute caused by excessive moisture present when the goods arrive at a possibly distant destination.

Conditioning-houses are primarily for the conditioning of tops and yarns, but they fulfil other functions. Tops are sampled and examined for their proportion of oil. Yarns are reeled to determine the reality of their marked number or count, and are examined for twist and tested for strength. Piece goods are measured and analysed and their strength is tested. The gain of one party is the loss of another, and testing-houses are less used than they might be in matters affecting only home or local trade. Goods to be sent abroad on journeys long enough to allow of a material change in the original condition as to moisture are the ones most regularly subjected to official test. For their personal satisfaction spinners make their testings on apparatus of their own but to carry conviction to others it is necessary to have independent tests.

Wool material may be damaged at almost any point, and the placing of the blame on the right shoulders is often not an easy matter. The possible causes of mischief begin while the wool is still on the sheep's back and liable to injury by drought and insufficient feeding, or by the use of unsuitable sheep-dip. Delicts in sorting, scouring, combing, drawing, spinning, warp-sizing, weaving, or finishing, directly or indirectly, develop unpleasant consequences later on. Threads with the twist in the wrong direction, the mixture in the same cloth of weft that has been stored for long with weft fresh from the spindle, undue strains or tensions in weaving or finishing, exposure to mildew, and causes more insignificant-seeming in themselves produce effects most difficult to trace and bring home unquestionably to the party really responsible for their occurrence. In cases of technical difficulty choice lies between the services of scientific experts and the arbitration of practical men. Points in dispute are referred frequently to the private arbitration of some friend in the trade or are carried to the textile consultant for elucidation by the microscope and instruments of precision.

Testing as well as manufacturing is taught in the technical schools and most of those who rise nowadays in the industry owe something to one or other of these institutions. The larger colleges are uncommercial mills equipped with every variety of machinery adaptable to the local trade and each takes its colour from the needs of its locality. The fine Bradford Technical College attends especially to all that concerns worsted and a larger share of attention is bestowed on woollens in the still finer Textile Department of the Leeds University. Tweed production is the especial study of the South of Scotland Technical College, Galashiels, and each of the Yorkshire towns has its own premises for education in the needs and methods of the local industry. Instruction is given at nights in the smaller institutes, and by day and night lectures and demonstrations in the larger. The schools illustrate and explain the rationale of mill tasks and aim at the production of better workmen and more instructed managers. In school the workman is able to learn the detail of the processes anterior and supplementary to those in which he is engaged, to accustom himself to unfamiliar machinery, and to recognise the use and adaptability of different materials.

The schools have improved industrial respect for scientific method in testing and manufacturing, but the typical manufacturer refuses to submit to scientific criteria alone. His necessities require him to take raw material as he finds it, and, by such means as he can encompass, turn it to the best account. He demands standards which take heed of the practical difficulties of the situation, and give credit for what he has been able to do and not simply blame for failure to achieve a theoretical perfection. Although not without reason, the demand is one that becomes increasingly difficult to maintain in the face of scientific researches. His work employs several of the sciences—mechanics, chemistry, physics, and electricity, among others—and involves some problems that have been little investigated in the past and as to which the final verdict of scientific study is uncertain. The application of too rigorous or artificial a set of standards in testing is resisted and the tyranny of theory is impatiently borne in the mill.

The textile schools are less expected than at one time to turn out finished manufacturing men and the inevitable failure to do this incurs less reproach. Manufacturing involves much else than book-learning. Doing is of more importance than knowing in the mill, and the understanding of processes is an affair separate from the mastery of men. In school extraneous difficulties are brought to a minimum by the selection and preparation of the material and the presence of skilled advice. In the mill, where material has to be taken as it is found, and where troublesome details have to be met as and when they arise, there is a need for initiative which technical training does not supply as effectively as previous experience. The fact tempers the esteem in which the textile schools are held without seriously detracting from opinions as to their real utility.

CHAPTER IX

THE FINANCE OF THE INDUSTRY

Wool, more than many commodities, is produced, handled, manufactured, and sold by individual rather than by joint-stock enterprise. The grower is an individual trader far more often than he is the agent or manager of any pastoral limited company. Public companies and banks receive his wool and advance funds upon it pending its sale in one country or another, but the grower farms his own or his landlord's soil at his own risk. Again, the importer, wool merchant, or topmaker is usually a private trader, making arrangement with those who control publicly-subscribed money, but not one who has shareholders of his own. Manufacturing, too, is carried on far more by private hands than public companies in this country. On the Continent and in the United States large sums of shareholders' money are invested in woollen and worsted industry. Here the rule is that the funds are the manufacturer's own or those of his family or private partners. The fact that so many manufacturing firms add " limited " to their name implies no more than a wider adoption of private limited liability.

At this point the wool industry shows in some contrast against cotton, and it may be asked why the wool industries have found less need of outside assistance. Inquiry will show that the joint-stock principle in cotton is most prevalent in the spinning branch. In the weaving trade, in which one may start with relatively small means, cotton manufacturing is also principally in private control. Cotton is a larger and more standardised industry. The raw material is not more expensive, but the output and orders are larger and conditions in cotton spinning are more favourable to a large or moderately sized than to a small concern. Then a cotton spinning mill is equipped to take in raw cotton and perform all processes incidental to the production of yarn. There is no division—as in worsted—between the combing and the spinning branches. The smaller worsted trade, with its more irregular requirements and its division into two parts, gave an opening to men of smaller capital than that required in the cotton spinning trade. There is not much public money in the English wool industries because there has been little need of it.

Starting in a small way as comber or spinner a man was—and in spinning still is—able to keep his plant in a state of efficiency similar to that of his larger neighbours. As a woollen manufacturer a relatively few thousand pounds would buy the complete set of machinery necessary to make a living and allow the manufacturer to find a groove of his own. The public companies in the wool industry have been formed more often to take over established enterprises than to promote new ones, and it is for the former purpose that public money can the more readily be found. The materials bought and manufactured are costly, and with the sums at their disposal beginners, in Yorkshire at any rate, could not have succeeded so without substantial aid from the banks. Bank overdrafts on the security of purchases of wool, mill premises, and machinery, have been more liberal than in some parts of the country and have enabled the industry to dispense with other help.

The working capital required in manufacturing is conditioned by the length of time taken in passing goods through their process and by the terms of credit in vogue. Wool sells at auction for cash, and tops are sold for cash in seven days, subject to four months' discount (*i.e.*, fourpence per £ = one penny per £ per month). Yarn is paid for about a month after delivery, the terms varying with local usage up to two months. Cloth is sold normally, on monthly terms which extend sometimes to two or three months; or is sold under exceptional discount for cash. In the high-class tweed and worsted trade there are "season's terms" for cloth under which two payments are made annually, one for the spring and the other for the autumn deliveries, and these settlements are not always in cash but are prolonged by bills. The long terms in the business in expensive suitings limit competition and help to maintain prices, but also they aggravate failures and increase the sum of working capital required. Obviously, a manufacturer who has to pay cash for raw material about twelve months before he himself will be paid for goods, has need of a heavier capital than one whose receipts and payment nearly balance in point of time. Dr. Oliver, a well-known Scottish authority, calls £40,000 not an extravagant sum to sink in a mill of fifty looms in the present state of the tweed trade. The amount is fully ten times as much as is necessary for the same number of looms when the yarn is bought and worsted cloth is sold on short credit.

The worsted trade in its later development has opened opportunities to the "small man" who can get a portion of his machinery on credit. The room or mill is rented and the rent in some cases includes engine-power. With five or ten thousand worsted spindles or thirty or forty looms, the beginner has a fair start. There are "manufacturers" and "spinners" without looms and without spindles who buy yarns and send them to a commission weaver, or buy tops and put them out to a commission spinner. The arrangement has both good points and bad. The owner of the material is freed from the shackles of machinery which clamours to be fed with work be times good or bad. On the other hand, the mechanical processes are either not so well done or so cheaply done as by the fully-equipped manufacturers. The system is of convenience to those who have not capital enough (*a*) to buy and treat material, and (*b*) those who have money for material but not for plant. The existence of the commission worker is of advantage, too, to the spinner or manufacturer who does not wish to extend his mill. Keeping his own machinery in full work at all times and sending his surplus to be treated outside, he avoids those dead expenses which go so far to neutralise the profits from the mill.

The combing and the dyeing trade are both syndicated, and combing, at least, offers fewer opportunities to the small man. A wave of syndication or combination spread over textile industry in the late 'nineties. The signal was the amalgamation in 1896 of the strongest concerns in the sewing cotton industry under the name J. P. Coats, Ltd. The formation of the English Sewing Cotton Company followed, and in 1898 the Fine Cotton Spinners' Association was formed. The success of these led to the promotion of the Bradford Dyers' Association in 1898, the Yorkshire Woolcombers' Association in the following year, and the British Cotton and Wool Dyers' Association in 1900. These concerns, with the knitting yarn "combine" known as J. & J. Baldwin & Partners, Isaac Holden & Sons, woolcombers, John Crossley & Sons, carpet manufacturers, and a few others are almost alone as holders of considerable sums of public capital.

The "combine" movement after a brisk life as a

popular craze suffered a reaction. Affairs began to go ill. The Yorkshire Woolcombers' Association, with its £1,931,800 of nominal capital, acquired 716 wool combs, the property of certain commission combers and topmakers. The thirty commission combers for their 565 combs were paid £914,794, and the eight topmakers for their 151 combs and incidental trade connections, were paid £880,562. The preference shares, applied for ten times over, and the debentures, applied for three times over by a hungry public, were waste paper in five years. The modestly capitalised Woolcombers, Ltd., arose from its ashes and, after passing the first year's dividend, has returned substantial ones since. The British Cotton and Wool Dyers' Association, engaged in dyeing tops and yarn, has in eleven years paid four dividends of 2 to 2½ per cent. per annum. Minor combinations have fallen into financial disrepute and hence it has come that the grand combination of worsted spinners has never materialised in fact. The combine was to have had a capital of £18,000,000 and to have been the largest of them all. It is doubtless true to say that no combine could buy the best mills in the trade, and that the capital would not be subscribed for a scheme that would involve the inclusion of a number of inferior businesses at prices in excess of their marketable worth.

The Bradford Dyers' Association, the head of the piece-dyeing trade and associated chiefly with dress goods and linings, with its £5,000,000 of nominal capital and debenture power for £1,500,000 more, has been a consistently successful concern. It has the competition of a dozen or more independent dyers, and in the matter of prices and the systematisation of work has done what personal agreement among unsyndicated dyers conspicuously failed to do. There is reason for agreeing that concentration and collective effort have in its case yielded good results technically and commercially. The failure of some, the struggle and belated success of others, and the discontent of some vendors with an unaccustomed control, have taught many lessons. The tendency twards universal combination, which flourished openly until 1900, has been effectively checked. The general or unsyndicated business is carried on in an atmosphere of free competition, but in an arena in which each has his special place and special aim. The conflict is not of everyone against everyone else, but a sectionalised competition, and the competitors have not heavy financial obligations to carry.

In Canada a common measure of the capitalisation of a woollen worsted mill is the value of the annual output. A mill with a capacity to produce 1,000,000 dollars worth of goods makes 1,000,000 dollars its nominal capital. To attract subscription of its preference stock, common stock is given away as a bonus with the preferred shares ; less with the idea that it will ever carry a dividend than in the hope that it will one day command a marketable value. The capital in the English privately-owned mill is the cash value that has actually been sunk in it, less the amount by which this sum has been periodically written down. The writing-off is done with such thoroughness as suits the taste of the individual but, in any case, a very different principal sum remains to that obtained by accepting the turnover for one year as the amount upon which to pay interest. The matter has an obvious bearing on the price at which goods can be sold and the ability of British producers to compete effectively in all markets.

The absence of inflation of capital, the ability to raise money at 4 or 5 per cent. instead of at 6 or 7 per cent., the cheapness of coal, the cheapness of building, the purchase of machinery at its first cost instead of at a price increased by heavy packing, freight, and customs charges, the abundant supplies of soft water, the assistance of an atmosphere friendly to spinning, and weaving, stand the British woollen and worsted industry in excellent stead. These advantages, if small singly, are cumulative and not unworthy of mention in the same breath as the apt and docile labour, the thoroughly sensible and conscientious workmanship which the British manufacturer commands. Stress is laid on the cheapness of British labour, and it is clear that woollen and worsted work is less remunerative to the operative than work in cotton factories. By the side of Continental wages, British woollen wages are high and are not as low in relation to American wages as is sometimes represented. What is more important than price is that the service rendered is of the best kind and unsurpassed by that of workmen anywhere.

CHAPTER X

COMBINATION AND WAGES

COMBINATION, whether among masters or men in the wool manufacturing industries is weak and presumably because conditions have not been highly favourable to either. Trade unionism does not find its most congenial soil among young women, who, with children, form a large part of the operative class. Nor does the topographical distribution of the parts of the industry favour the combination of workpeople. The woollen trade is carried on largely by scattered groups of workers of different grades, working at separate tasks, and living in isolation from the similar groups employed not many miles away. Where the industry is most centred, and where men are employed in relatively large masses, the unions are strongest in point of number. The overlookers in the worsted spinning and weaving mills and the power-loom tuners of the woollen trade are the non-commissioned officers of the industry and have associations of their own, necessarily limited in membership, which are still highly effective in regulating conditions of service. Cloth pressers and warp dressers belong to select trades which also have societies that are strong enough for their work.

The wool sorters are a relatively strong organised body, and the combers have attained and lost again a considerable strength. The willeyers and fettlers employed in the carding departments, form a fairly strong union along with the weavers employed in Huddersfield. The dyers' unions have an all but complete grasp on the trade, and in general the unions have extorted the employers' recognition. In the dyeing trade a Wages Board and a collective agreement with the Bradford Dyers' Association make an important addition to the resources of trade unionism, and in the combing trade a collective agreement between the employers and the union served while it lasted greatly to increase the union's powers. The recognition accorded to the unions is rather private than official It is true that the Huddersfield employers have an association expressly for dealing with affairs of wages and hours, but there has not been in the wool manufacturing trades such a display of opposing force as has called into being the numerous cotton manufacturers' associations and federations.

The Chambers of Commerce in the manufacturing districts are the chief associations of employers and they are loosely formed for many other objects than collective dealing with the grievances of the employed. The Chambers maintain Conciliation Boards registered at the Board of Trade for the purpose of intermediation in acute cases of dispute. They provide a platform for the airing of views on all subjects allied with manufacture, but are not comparable with bodies formed to compensate members who may be faced with strikes, nor are their judgments binding upon the individual members. The combination of employers in the cotton and engineering industries has followed on the combination of workmen, and in the wool manufacture the cause has hitherto been insufficient to produce the effect.

Industrial conditions, too, have hitherto been unfavourable to associations of employers having for their object the maintenance of prices. Apart from the "combines" in which there is a fusion of capital, no organisations with this end in view have had any prolonged existence. The failure of collective efforts to limit price-cutting formed a cogent reason for the amalgamation of firms into the textile combines. Dyeing and combing call indeed for skill, economy, and good management but they are only two processes out of several, and combing, at least, has less to do with determining the individuality of goods than have spinning and manufacturing. The individual choice of raw materials, and the individual ways of going about the methods of manufacture result in giving to articles, nominally alike, a distinguishable character of their own, differentiating the products of one manufacturer from the productions of another. These fine differences can only seem inconsiderable to those who do not know the by-ways of trade, and it is because of one or another of these that one make of article is preferred or insisted upon. The maintenance of a distinct individuality in the goods turned out leads in turn to an individualism of demand and to inequalities in price which do not contribute to the harmonious working of an arrangement to preserve a certain minimum. Perhaps in no industry have these distinctions been utterly abolished and in the wool industries, with their infinite varieties of production, individuality has an exceptional play, which, if it obstructs combination, at the same time removes some of the necessity for joint action in order to maintain a remunerative level of price.

Combination for these more pressing needs being either absent or slight, it is natural that union for less urgent objects should be slight also. The wool trade has its fraternal associations of dealers meeting partly for social purposes, partly for the discussion of common business aims. Spinners and manufacturers are almost without formal organisations for that purpose. There is a private interchange of opinion on market-day, or such other occasions as throw acquaintances together. Textile societies exist principally in connection with the technical schools and their main purpose is the reading and discussion of papers. The Textile Institute of Manchester is the nearest approach to such Institutes as exist in connection with the metal trades for the dissemination of technical information among manufacturers, as distinct from learners or students. Combination—in short—is not a spontaneous growth in any department, and the fact is one that it is more customary to accept than to deplore.

Among the trade unions in the worsted and woollen trades there is a trend towards closer co-operation and, carried beyond a certain point, this movement might be expected to produce the same results as the federation of local unions has produced elsewhere. Without very considerable aid from trade unionism, wages have risen to a height certainly lower than that of the Lancashire cotton industry, but higher than in most other countries.

Taking together the men, women, and children employed in worsted and woollen factories in this Kingdom, the average earnings per head of wage workers is some £40 per year. The figure is that ascertained in 1906 in course of the Board of Trade inquiry into textile wages, and any change that has occurred since is in the direction of an increase. The years 1908-1911 have been years of rising wages in which many thousands of operatives obtained advances of some 10 per cent. It follows that the figures of 1906 require some correction to bring them into touch with actuality, and as the wages go up more often than they come down, it is probable that the succeeding Government inquiry will disclose at least as great an improvement as that between 1886 and 1906, in which period wages of men increased

15 per cent. and wages of women 10 per cent. These advances in wages have been given largely without strikes and without public notice, and, pending the taking of a further census of wages, their effect cannot be exactly appreciated.

In 1906 the average man employed in a woollen or worsted factory earned in a full week 26s. 10d., and the average woman, 13s. 10d. The average boy or girl, working half-time in the factory, earned 3s. 8d. per week, and the whole-time boy earned 10s. 2d., and the whole-time girl 9s. 3d. The amounts are made better than they look by the fact that the mills afford work for every member of the household, and that normally the labour of young women and young persons is in greater demand than supply. The average covers many variations from the extremes, but taking the case of a family where a father, two daughters and two sons work in the mill, there is a family income of 65s. 8d.; not a bad one in towns where cottage rents are cheap and food is purveyed at closely competitive prices or bought at substantially cost price from the co-operative stores.

The wages vary by districts as well as by occupations, and the 1906 return shows an average for men of only 21s. 9d. per week in the West of England and of 29s. 2d. in Leeds. The West of England also produced the lowest average wage for women, 11s. 3d. a week, as against the average 17s. 1d. in Huddersfield and 18s. 6d. in the Scottish Border counties. Discrepancies nearly as marked occur between districts much closer at hand and are rather encouraged to continue by the system of family employment. A family is less mobile than an individual and less ready to change its home. There is relatively little movement of workpeople out of the areas of lower wages into the districts where higher rates obtain, and still less is there a movement of mill machinery out from the districts where labour is superficially dear. It is exceedingly costly to remove and re-erect machines, and the lower-priced labour is not invariably the more economical. Weaving wages are some 20 per cent. more in Huddersfield than in Bradford, but the Huddersfield work is more intricate, is done without the accompaniment of much waste or spoilt material and consequently without an undue subsequent cost in mending.

The West of England does not produce cheaper cloth than the West Riding of Yorkshire, despite its paper advantage in wages. The case is far to the contrary, and it is scarcely divulging a secret to say that some nominally West of England cloths are Yorkshire spun and Yorkshire woven. Some real differences in earnings can exist where competition is indirect. It does not seriously matter to employers whether they pay more or less wages than manufacturers who are not working for the same market and making similar goods. Nor does it matter whether wages are apparently high if the real cost is low. The true measure is efficiency, and apart from advantage in this direction a manufacturer gains some reflected glory from his address. To be a Huddersfield worsted manufacturer, or a Galashiels or Hawick tweed manufacturer, is enough in itself to raise the individual out of the ruck of some sorts of competition and to justify the asking of a certain price. Situation in the established homes of the industry does not in these later times guarantee a sufficiency of skilled help, but at least it brings some choice of apt workers skilled in the particular kinds of work peculiar to the neighbourhood.

Once it was water that a manufacturer sought in looking for a site to build a mill, and from the earliest times the mills have clustered round the streams that fed them originally with power and constantly with water for scouring and dyeing. Now it is for sufficient relays of labour that he must look, and already the worsted spinning industry is being tempted towards new colliery districts where men are well employed and local work for women is absent.

CHAPTER XI

STANDARDISATION OF QUALITIES

The absence of any "futures" market is a significant feature of the wool trade in England. There are exchanges in three Continental countries where wool or tops of a standard grade can be bought or sold in unlimited quantities, and where transactions can be rounded off by the payment of differences instead of by the delivery of goods. Tops can be bought in England for delivery at future dates, and an arrangement for weekly or monthly deliveries to the spinner is usual. Yarns are bought regularly on contract at a certain basis price with "particulars down" or particulars (of count, twist, warping) to follow. The transaction is in goods, not in paper, and a delivery of goods is required.

There are conveniences in such a system as prevails almost universally in the sale of cotton, at Roubaix, Antwerp, and Leipzig in the sale of tops, and at Havre in the buying and selling of raw wool. Futures can be used to remove the gambling element in transactions requiring long to complete. Prices are as liable to fall as to rise while wool is on the water in course of its long voyage from the producing countries to the manufacturing centres, and the importer is exposed to the risk of a loss which he cannot conveniently insure against or control. By selling paper "futures" of the same month that his cargo is due to arrive or to be sold, he safeguards himself. The loss on the actual sale is compensated by the gain on the nominal transaction made in the terminal market. He sells his wool at a lower rate than he reckoned on, but buys back his " bear " of futures at a lower price than that at which he sold and collects the difference in his favour. A spinner embarking on a contract to deliver yarn at distant dates exposes himself to a risk of an advance in the price of raw material, which he may or may not be able to cover by contracting with a maker of tops. The futures market offers him an opportunity of insurance. By buying paper futures at the price of the day against his requirement of material months ahead, he secures himself of a gain on the one hand approximately equal in amount to his loss upon the other.

The advantages are counterbalanced by drawbacks. The standardisation of a grade of tops and the abolition of the need to take delivery, throw the market open to speculation by outsiders who have no technical knowledge of wool and no substantial stake in the industry. The standard contract top becomes a gambler's counter, and transactions take place which have no real relations to the natural requirement of trade. The defenders of the system maintain that in the long run unlimited buying and selling tends to steady prices, but this is scarcely the industrial view. English spinners will have none of a system which they regard as favourable rather to the professional speculator than to the industrial user of wool. On the Continent it is complained by manufacturers that the exchange transactions cause a decline in the quality of tops and an over-production of inferior tops, made to suit exchange requirements rather than the necessities of industry. For these effects the rules of the exchanges and the standard type adopted may be partly answerable. The graver objections are that terminal dealings disturb prices unduly, create an artificial dearness, and lend an undesired aid to the finance of large speculations.

The Leipzig futures market is under an official ban, and may not publish its transactions, but the quotations for South American merino wool at Havre, and for standard merino tops at Antwerp and Roubaix-Tourcoing are regularly printed. There are set forth in a table below, representative quotations stretching ahead for a year.

	Wool. Havre Merino, type 36%		Tops Antwerp, type B.		Tops. Roubaix-Tourcoing, Merino standard type.	
Deliveries	Oct. 28.	Oct. 21.	Oct. 28.	Oct. 21.	Oct. 27	Oct. 20.
October	159	156	–	5.25	–	5.32½
November	159	155½	5.30	5.22½	5.37½	5.27½
December	159	155½	5.27½	5.22½	5.35	5.27½
January.	159	155½	5.27½	5.20	5.32½	5.22½
February	162	159	5.25	5.17½	5.30	5.22½
March	162	159	5.22½	5.15	5.25	5.17½
April	162	159	5.22½	5.12½	5.27½	5.17½
May	162	159	5.22½	5.12½	5.25	5.15
June	162	159	5.20	5.12½	5.25	5.15
July	162	159	5.20	5.10	5.22½	–
August	162	159	5.17½	5.10	5.22½	–
September	162	159	5.17½	5.10	–	–

The prices are in francs and centimes per kilogramme for tops and per 100 kilogrammes for wool.

While the Continental quotations are far from being a perfect index to the future of the wool market, the prices are not disregarded in summing up the market situation at any given time. Reduction to a common standard makes comparison relatively easy, whereas comparisons between prices of raw wools may be seriously misleading to those who have not seen the particular lots, or are not in a position to appreciate their peculiar merits and defects. It is the custom, therefore, of brokers and market reporters to deal rather in percentages than in definite prices. "Merino grease sells at an advance of 5 per cent. as compared with the close of the last series of sales "—write a firm of London brokers—" Scoureds show scarcely any advance. Cross-breds are 5 per cent. dearer, the finer lots showing the advance most. Capes are fully up to last sales." The method lends itself to dispute, and eminent firms are found varying in their opinion as to whether the rise is really only $7\frac{1}{2}$ or as much as 10 per cent., but it has conveniences and cannot be superseded without reducing the wools compared to some common denominator.

Similarly with the semi-manufactured article, tops, there is a certain latitude of doubt as to prices. Five topmakers may quote as many fractionally different prices for 60's tops on the same day, each quoting for his own 60's and each offering substantially equal value. Consequently in dealing with tops it is often more illuminating to hear that the market is a penny up or a halfpenny down, than that any nominal quality is offered at a stated price. The information means that there has been a general movement of that extent irrespective of the nicer considerations of quality that are only appreciable at first hand.

It is the settled policy of those who handle wool in this country to make participation by outsiders difficult rather than easy, and to leave to the buyer the responsibility of forming his own judgment. The " guaranteed yield " system on which South American wools are sometimes bought is a foreign innovation, devised primarily for the convenience of the Continental buyers, who are the chief consumers of this material, but now availed of by English firms. The South American wool exporters submit samples, quoting a price per lb. representing the net price of the scoured clean wool, *i.e.*, after the removal of all grease and dirt. On the arrival of the bales the importer examines them and declares whether he accepts them as a good delivery or demands a test. In the latter event fifteen bales, or ten in every 100, are sent for sorting, scouring, and combing to some independent establishment agreed upon mutually. The buyer, in demanding the guarantee, submits to pay an extra charge of 1 per cent. upon the gross value of the invoice. Should the tests show a deficit the seller is bound to make the amount good, and if it should prove that the yield is better than that of the contract the buyer has to pay the seller the difference. The 1 per cent. charge ensures that the seller should not be held answerable for any underyield within that limit, and restrains the buyer from making vexatious claims.

So that the final cost is right it matters not at all to the buyer at what price the raw wool is invoiced, and the nominal invoice price is adjusted by the seller to such a rate as will bring in the particular material at the basis price stated in the order form. The forms of contract in use for this purpose vary in detail but contain some clause like the following:

"............bales............fleece wool, similar to sample No....... at............ per lb., on the basis of—Tops and noils, oil combed, without expenses c.i.f. Liverpool, Manchester, or Hull." This is followed by a statement of the allowances to be made for moisture and for oil in the tops and noils in question. The elimination of uncertainty as to net yield does not carry very far in smoothing the path for the outsider, and is the furthest measure taken in regular English practice.

CHAPTER XII

PRODUCTS AND BY-PRODUCTS

THE products of the wool industries are classified for official purposes as

- Wool, sorted, blended, etc.
  - Sheep or lambs' wool
  - Other sorts
- Woollen rags, carbonized, dyed, etc.
  - Tops
  - Noils
  - Flocks
  - Waste
  - Shoddy, Mungo, etc.
- Yarns (all wool or mixed)
  - Woollen (carded)
  - Worsted (combed or carded)
  - Alpaca and Mohair
  - Other hair or wool
- Woollen Tissues (all wool or mixed)
- Worsted
  - Broad = 54 in. wide or upwards
  - Narrow = less than 54 in. wide
  - Heavy = over 11 oz. per square yard
  - Light = under 11 oz.
- Worsted stuffs, Dress goods, Linings, Lastings, etc.
- Damask, Tapestry, Furniture stuffs
- Wool, Mohair Plushes
- Flannels and Delaines
- Carpets (other than rugs)
- Rugs (other than travelling rugs)
- Blankets

Shawls
Coverlets, Travelling Rugs, and Wrappers
Wool, Mohair Laces, and Smallwares
Unenumerated.

The divisions are assimilable with those adopted in the import and export returns which are constructed to show the totals by main classes. The division into broad and narrow in the case of woollen and worsted fabrics is necessary in interpreting the yardage. Trouserings are made from 27/30 ins. wide, and suitings 54/58 ins. wide, and one yard of the one is equivalent substantially to two of the other. The distinction between heavy and light is necessitated by the extreme variation of weights per yard, with the thin tropical worsted weighing, perhaps, 10 oz. per running yard at one end of the scale and cloths weighing two pounds and more to the yard at the other. Stuffs, linings, and dress goods are variable in width and weight but vary within narrower limits; their general character is too different to allow them to be classed with the wider and heavier fabrics. The succeeding items in the list are distinct from the foregoing and from each other, and correspond with cleavages in the trade.

"Woollen tissues" comprehend everything from the highest class of tweeds, beaver, melton, and billiard cloth in the "all-wool" division down to the poorest combination of cotton warp and shoddy weft in the "mixed" division. "Worsted Tissues" include a range of articles wide but less extreme. The fine worsted suiting of the best merino wool, the harsher cloths from crossbreds, and the union fabric made with a cotton warp or weft, fall into the one classification or the other. Stuffs and dress-goods cover rich and poor fabrics equally, from the finest wool and mohair goods to those that are all but all cotton.

GREASE RECOVERY FROM WOOL SUDS

Besides the cloths for personal wear and those for decorative purposes, are those specially for mechanical use. The felts and blankets of the paper maker, calico printer, and lithographic and letterpress printers are examples in one direction. Again, there is the considerable quantity of coarse, strong fabrics made of wool and hair for press and filter cloths, as used by oil pressers, and the smaller quantity of hair cloth woven into thick multiplex fabrics to make driving belts for machines. A certain amount of yarn is spun annually not for weaving into fabrics but to make the "healds" or cords, without which looms would not weave. The flocks used for stuffing mattresses and furniture are manufactured in a limited sense, and are rather in the nature of by-products. The case is different with the highly manufactured article, dolls' hair, of which a few mills in Bradford produce some 30,000 lbs. a week. The wool chosen is good, springy, lustrous English wool from wether sheep. It is scoured, combed, dyed to delicate shades, and put through a mechanical curling operation before being passed to the manufacturers of complete dolls.

The wool industries consume their own chief products, for the waste of one process is the raw material of another. Opportunities of further economies in the utilisation of spent material are necessarily restricted, yet the industries have some. In Belgium, more than in England, wool scourers steep the raw wool in water with a view to dissolving and subsequently recovering and selling the natural potash salts present as an impurity in the material. The recovery of wool grease is a common process, dictated not only by considerations of economy, but by the necessity of conciliating the sewage authorities or the Rivers Board. The recovery is made both from the suds formed in scouring wool, and those created in scouring pieces. The sud is passed into a tank and treated with common vitriol, causing the fats to separate out and rise in the form of scum. The clear water is passed away through a chain of filters, and the grease, scraped from the floor of the tank, is enveloped in canvas squares. The grease goes to the hydraulic press, is heated in a steam jacket, and put under pressure, causing the oily constituent to exude. The fluid is passed into barrels and is either sold to distillers of grease or thinned with some lighter oil and returned to the mill for use again in oiling wool for carding. When refined, the wool fat, or lanoline, becomes a basis for ointment and an article of toilet. The hard cake resting behind in the press cloth is used for fuel and for manuring hop gardens.

CHAPTER XIII

THE *PERSONNEL* OF THE INDUSTRY

THE general survey would be incomplete without some brief consideration of the multitude of widely different persons engaged in carrying on the great wool industry. The account may begin with the shepherd who, in this country at least, is commonly a skilled, intelligent, and faithful man, whose remuneration in cash and in kind is something like a pound a week for knowing all that is to be known, and doing all that is to be done, in the care of his charges. He knows his sheep by their faces, and can identify the parents of his lambs. He recognises and treats their ailments, and in lambing time works both day and night. A bit of a surgeon, more than a bit of a butcher, a useful man with the shears or on the turnips, an expert in the use of dogs, a good haggler, a good judge, and very often a natural philosopher, the modern shepherd in these islands gets less recognition than he deserves.

In picturesque qualities the homely shepherd may be outclassed by the station hand of Australia, the half-castes of South America, and the nomad shepherds of the East. He is admittedly less expert with the shears than the professional shearers in Australia who make their two pounds a day by exceeding ability in the use of the clipping machines which have replaced the old tong-like shears. Wool raising is not a separate industry affording play for sub-division and specialisation in this country. But extending the view to the whole wool-producing world, a motley legion of people are found in it. Besides the station hands and riders and lonely hut shepherds, who see no other man for a month at a stretch, there are the port workers, the pressers or " dumpers " of wool, the auctioneers and brokers, and clerks. Back in the country are the storekeepers whose whole livelihood pivots on the production of wool and the sale of wool packs, twine, sheep-dip, medicine, and station rations.

On our own side of the water, in the places where preparation for manufacture begins, are the wool warehousemen to be seen leaning from crane doors, clad in the uniform of their calling, the long blue and white smock, or " checker-brat." Inside the warehouses, working at screen-topped tables facing cool north lights, are the wool sorters examining and breaking up the fleece. If they work with the scheduled dangerous wools and hairs they work under set precautions with a downward draught continually carrying off the dust that their manipulation of the wool dislodges. Anthrax, or woolsorter's disease, contracted from Eastern wools and hair, is their principal and, perhaps, their only considerable foe. Their work is healthful, and if the stationary position leaves the sorter exposed to cold in winter he has at least the advantage of a cool atmosphere in summer.

The sorter, sure of his thirty-two and sixpence a week during the larger part of the year, has a position enviable by comparison with that of the comber. The combing man and woman are at the bottom of the ladder of the industry and, although circumstanced more happily than at one time, they suffer from the pressure of the unskilled labour market. The sheds in busy times run both night and day ; and while the day work is regular the night work is casual, and sought as a refuge employment by the time-expired soldier, the tradesman out of work, the unfortunate, the dissolute, and unskilled. Toiling with scanty clothing in temperatures ranging up to 100 degrees, exhausted by their spell, ill-clad, ill-nourished, and unhappy, the combers present a sorry contrast with the open-air workers upon the sheep farms, earning possibly lower wages.

Much against the will of schoolmasters, parents in the Yorkshire worsted spinning towns continue to send their children into the mill under the half-time rules. By the age of twelve, if able to pass severe educational tests, children are allowed to enter the mills working alternately in the mornings and afternoons, and for the rest of the day attending school. They take off and put on spinning bobbins, remove the accumulating fly-waste from the spinning rollers, and learn the delicate art of piecing together ends of worsted yarn. From the standpoint of industrial perfection, the earlier the child begins to practise the suppleness and deftness necessary in making a neat job of piecing broken yarn the better. A girl makes a better spinner for life by beginning at the age of eight than by beginning at nine, and better by beginning at nine, ten, or eleven than at the age of twelve. Of the older operatives and employers hundreds still alive did begin at eight and are unable to realise that they suffered hardship.

The children clacking in their clogs, white smocks and shawls or mufflers, off to the mill at 6 a.m., and coming home again at noon, remain one of the distinctive features of the Yorkshire worsted spinning business. Inside the mill they are comfortably warm in an atmosphere that even in winter is maintained at or about seventy. In the dark of a cold, wet morning, it is possible to feel that the advantage of an early initiation into mill life may be exaggerated. All but a few of the boys perforce leave the spinning department, the girls stay on and graduate as minders of spinning frames, earning wages corresponding with the number of frames tended. Automatic doffers for spinning frames and the protests of school authorities foreshadow the eventual disappearance of the half-timer.

For men, worsted spinning provides work chiefly as overlookers, who have the oversight of the work done and are responsible for the changing of wheels and the setting of machines. All the mechanism of the drawing department is adjusted to a calculated end, and different adjustments of speeds and distances are made for different classes of material and counts of yarn. The changes are made by substituting wheels, and the complete overlooker is a man of figures, using logarithms and the slide rule; he is more or less of a mechanic and a tactful disciplinarian. The overlooker is paler and sparer than the worker out of doors, but of the right stamina for the mill. His occupation is interesting to men of the right bent, and in some countries an English overlooker is better paid and more esteemed than at home. Specimen Yorkshire overlookers are to be found in nearly all the worsted spinning countries. They work in France, Germany, Holland, Belgium, Austria, Russia, North America—indeed, wherever there are British worsted spinning machines.

Of quite a similar type is the weaving overlooker, or power-loom tuner, as the woollen trade prefers to call him. His forte is a complete understanding of the complex mechanism of looms, an ability to understand and remedy their disorders and, on being given a ground-plan on squared paper, an ability to mount a loom to weave any given design. Overlookers, if they are studious, fortunate, and able, grow up into managers who assume full mechanical control and complete charge of the workpeople. But to make a complete weaving manager one has usually to be also a designer.

Designing calls for a double aptitude for the designer is the architect of cloths. His designs may be replicas of those of other men and demand no more than a technical knowledge of cloth structures, in which case the designer is more a builder than an architect. It is the business of designers of the higher class to add to mere mechanical ingenuity, taste, invention, and skill in detecting and forestalling the trend of public fancy. The designer in the fancy trades may make or break the mill, and large salaries are paid to the best designers. Those who are gifted salesmen, and managers as well as designers, may earn more, but the range of salaries is from £100 to £1,000 a year.

Weaving employs many women and few men. Trial patterns on hand looms, the most expensive worsteds and woollens are woven by men, but two out of three of all the persons in and about the weaving sheds are women. Female labour is cheaper than male although less resourceful, and cheapness and its concomitant abundance, explain the presence of women in the weaving shed. The racket of a hundred looms dismays a visitor. Shouting barely enables him to hear his own voice, but the weaver's ear is attuned to the rattle and uproar and heeds it as little as the city dweller the sound of the traffic. The sheds are most often bare and whitewashed, well lit because of the need of the work and warmed to 60 or 65 degrees F. There is no " steaming " of the atmosphere as in certain branches of the cotton trade, and the operative minds only one or two looms. The monotony of the task of tending the machine is broken by the minor incidents and accidents, the necessity for replenishing weft, watching the pattern to see that all is well, and the restarting when anything is amiss and the loom " bangs off." The work is more popular among women than domestic service, and in

By kind permission of] [*Messrs. Priestley, Ltd.*

GIRL WEAVING AT LOOM

some quarters is more popular than work with the sewing machine. The work is not beyond the strength of women, and not incompatible with good health and good looks. The woman weaver is less boisterous and coarse than some of the operatives of thirty years ago, and more solicitous of her personal appearance when at work. Clogs and shawls are vanishing, the weaver comes and goes in her third or second-best, and on Sundays vies with the birds in finery.

Taking the woollen, worsted, and shoddy industries as a whole, the proportion of men employed to women employed is roughly as two is to three. The women do the light and routine work, the tasks that call rather for patience and deftness than initiative. The men do the rough work and that which puts most tax on the intelligence. Men officer the industry and women leave it to be married or remain in the ranks. Seldom, indeed, do they rise to positions of control.

The male weavers retain marks of their heritage from those who worked at the handlooms, and although unable now to play cricket in mid-week and steal the lost hours from the night, they are a steady and an independent breed. Their work is pleasanter than that of the willeyers and fettlers who man the card-rooms, but less remunerative than that of the spinner of the woollen trade, or of the warp dressers or the twisters-in who thread and fasten the warps into the looms. A less skilled class of men find work in the dyehouse, and, at least in the commission dyeing works, their employment is precarious. The foreman dyer accepts responsibility for the colours and the materials to use, and the dyehouse labourer fetches and carries, or with one hand lightly steers the passing cloth in or out of the machine. The dyehouse atmosphere is one of steam and fumes, and its floor is slopped with coloured water. Its machines, filled with boiling liquids, make it on the whole an uninviting place. It is possible to be more at ease in the warehouse examining the cloths that are the outcome of so many operations and trying processes.

In reaching the manufactured stage wool employs many, and in passing into consumption it employs many more. The woollen merchant, with his warehousemen, clerks, and staff of travellers, the tailor and dressmaker with their workpeople and assistants, and the factory clothiers with their thousands of hands, and the machine knitters are parties to the industry rather than camp-followers. The list might be indefinitely extended by inclusion of the allied trades—the makers of looms and spindles, the tanners of the leather that is extensively consumed in combing and spinning, the oil, soap, and chemical people, the makers of aniline dye wares, the bag-makers, paper-makers, case-makers, and printers directly dependent on the wool production who constitute an army in themselves. Let it suffice to deal shortly with the bare beginnings of the great distributive system, the merchants who set the goods rolling down the long incline on their way to the ultimate consumer.

The customers of the mills are of two broad classes. The home-trade merchant, serving, and in some measure financing, the tailor or draper, is distinguished from the shipper or shipping merchant in buying to stock. He orders in advance of the season, buying in large quantities and selling in small. The shipper, supplying wholesale merchants or clothiers abroad, buys to cover orders as they are received, sends out a ceaseless stream of patterns and despatches travellers to the markets he especially cultivates. The shipper's position is closer to that of an agent, and it is in seeking and offering the goods that distant parties are likely to buy, examining them before shipment, seeing to their proper packing and the routine of forwarding and finance that he is useful and, indeed, indispensable, in all but exceptional circumstances. The textile manufacturer is remoter from retailer and from consumer than manufacturers in some other trades, for reasons not difficult to understand. The retailer wants small quantities and large variety; the manufacturer wants orders for large quantities of preferably a small variety. The wholesale house bridges the gulf, giving the manufacturer orders of the size he needs for economical working, and giving the retailer the choice of a wide selection. The manufacturer is comparatively little known outside his own locality and direct customers. Woollen mills employing thousands of hands are less famed publicly, and on a wide scale than factories producing goods to not one-tenth of the value. Only the makers of particular specialities see fit to advertise, and for this there is a natural reason. The goods they make—cloth or yarn—are not turned out by them in the form ready for immediate consumption. The yarn must be turned into cloth and garments before arriving at the condition in which wool is principally wanted by the ultimate consumer.

The garment-maker advertises widely and boldly such articles as raincoats, and the hosiery manufacturers make increasing use of trade marks. The one sells a coat that is made in one season of one fabric and in the next of another. The hosiery manufacturer sells a garment that is little susceptible to fashionable influences. The dyer or finisher, who impresses upon cloth not his own property, the name and trade-mark of some special finish, draws attention to an effect which can be produced on any similar goods. Their position differs from that of manufacturers who have to

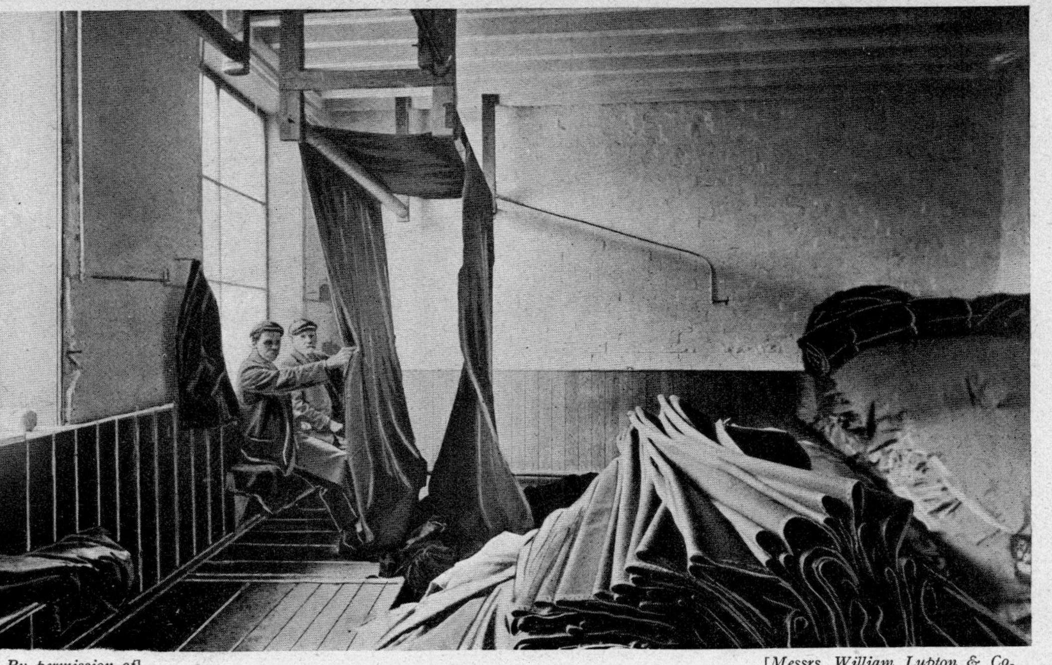

By permission of] [*Messrs. William Lupton & Co.*

FINAL EXAMINATION

produce different goods for different seasons, and to sell them in bulk to customers who object in most cases to deal in goods branded or advertised in any name but their own. The advertising of woollen and worsted fabrics may grow further in this country, and is growing in the United States, but essentially it is a method applicable more to profitable specialities of a relatively fixed character than to the drugs of the market or to fabrics which have only an evanescent demand. Meantime, outside their own circles, the identity of manufacturers is little known.

GLOSSARY

Alpaca	Hair of the Peruvian llama (Auchenia paco).
Back washing	The second scouring process given to tops.
Bale	Australasian bales of wool weigh about 3 cwts.; Argentine bales about 930 lbs.
Botany	Synonym for Merino wool; fine wool.
Burling	Removing surface imperfections from cloth.
Carding	The teasing-out of fibre by the aid of fine steel wire points set in rubber or leather foundations and mounted on cylinders.
Cashmere	Hair of the Kashmir goat; also a dress material made from the Botany wool; applied by tailors to worsted trouserings, etc.
Cheviot	Wool from Cheviot sheep. In Scotland a name applied to the coarser wools to distinguish them from "Saxony" or Merino.
Combing	The removal of short fibre accompanied by the ordering of the longer ones in parallel positions.
Condition	The proportion of water present in tops and yarns.
Crabbing	A treatment to prevent the shrinking or cockling of cloth in the subsequent processes of dyeing and finishing.
Cuttling	Plaiting cloth in folds.
Doubling	Twisting together two single yarns to make a two-fold.
Drawing	Preparing the combed top for the spinning frame by reducing it to "roving."
Ends	Warp threads.
Extract	Woollen material recovered by chemical means from mixtures containing vegetable matter.
Genapping or Gassing	Burning off the surface fibre from yarn to produce a more lustrous thread.
Gilling	An operation for straightening worsted fibre and intermixing differently coloured tops to secure an even admixture.
Hank	In worsted 7 wraps or leas of 80 yds. = 560 yds. In cotton and spun silk 7 leas of 120 yds. = 840 yds.
Hogg	A yearling sheep; hogg wool is the first clip from the animal.

LUSTRE	A name applied generically to the mohair alpaca and bright wool industry; specifically implies bright, long wools, principally English-grown.
MERINO	Wool of the Merino sheep; in hosiery a mixture of cotton and wool; the name of wool dress goods principally produced in France; certain rags are known as merinos.
MILLING	A process designed to felt or consolidate cloth or to break out ends of fibre from the yarn.
MIXTURE	Mixture shade in contradistinction to solid shade; formed by blending differently coloured loose fibres. A mixture effect in cloth is a varied but patternless one.
MOHAIR	Wool of the Angora goat (Capridae Angora).
MULE	Machine for producing a full, soft yarn.
MUNGO	Woollen fibre recovered from milled or hard cloth; mungo is shorter than shoddy.
NOIL	Short fibre removed by the woolcomb.
PACK	240 lbs. of wool.
PICKS	Weft threads.
RE-COMBING	A second combing given after tops have been dyed.
REGAIN	The natural or conventional allowance of moisture in tops and yarn; the difference between a state of bone dryness and the moister state due to absorption of atmospheric water.
ROVING	Lightly twisted sliver reduced in diameter in readiness for spinning.
SAXONY	The Scotch name for fine or merino wools.
SCOURING	Washing free from grease and dirt.
SHED	The parting formed in the warp threads during weaving to admit the shuttle.
SHODDY	The product of soft rags.
SIZING	Animal or vegetable matter applied to warps to reduce chafing in weaving.
SKEIN	Woollen yarn is numbered by skeins instead of by hanks. A Leeds or Huddersfield skein = 256 yds.
SKIN WOOL	Wool removed from sheep skins by sweating or fermentation.
SLIPE	Wool removed from sheepskins by the aid of lime.
SLIVER	Fibre arranged in a continuous loose rope or ribbon.
SLUBS	Thick places in yarn.
STUFFS	Light weight fabrics for linings and dresses, usually having cotton warps.

Tender	Material deficient in tensile strength.
Tentering	The operation of holding or stretching the width of cloth.
Top	The long fibre delivered by the wool comb.
Union	Denotes warp of one material, weft of another.
Wether	In opposition to hogg; wool from the second and subsequent annual shearing.
Woollen	Used in contradistinction to worsted, implies difference of material and of method of manufacture. Wastes, shoddy, and blends of material other than wool are referred to as "woollen" in opposition to "all wool."
Yolk	The grease in wool.

INDEX

THE END

Printed by Sir Isaac Pitman & Sons, Ltd., Bath
N—(1459)

AN ABRIDGED LIST OF THE

COMMERCIAL SERIES

OF

SIR ISAAC PITMAN & SONS, LTD.

1 AMEN CORNER, LONDON, E.C. *And at* BATH & NEW YORK.

SOLD BY ALL BOOKSELLERS THROUGHOUT THE WORLD

ARITHMETIC

First Steps in Commercial Arithmetic. By Arthur E. Williams, M.A., B.Sc. In crown 8vo, limp cloth, 80 pp. . . . . **8d.** net.

Business Arithmetic. Part I. In crown 8vo, cloth, 120 pp. . . . . **1s.**

Answers to Business Arithmetic Part I. Cloth . . . . **1s.**

Business Arithmetic. Part II. In crown 8vo, cloth, 144 pp. . . . . **1s. 6d.**

Answers to Business Arithmetic. Part II. Cloth . . . . **1s.**

Pitman's Complete Commercial Arithmetic. Contains Parts I and II above mentioned. In crown 8vo, cloth, 264 pp. . . . . **2s. 6d.**

Answers to Pitman's Complete Commercial Arithmetic. Whole cloth . . . . **1s. 6d.**

Pitman's Smaller Commercial Arithmetic. By C. W. Crook, B.A., B.Sc. In crown 8vo, cloth . . . . **1s.** net.

Answers to Smaller Commercial Arithmetic . . . . **1s.** net.

First Steps in Workshop Arithmetic. By H. P. Green, Head Arithmetic Master at Pitman's School. In crown 8vo, limp cloth, about 80 pp. . . . . **8d.** net.

Pitman's Complete Mercantile Arithmetic. With Elementary Mensuration. By H. P. Green, F.C.Sp.T., Head Arithmetic Master at Pitman's School. In crown 8vo, cloth gilt, with Key, 646 pp., **4s. 6d.** net. Complete book without Key, 600 pp., **4s.** net. Key separately, **1s.** net. Also in three parts. Part I, 300 pp., **2s. 6d.** net. Part II, 208 pp., **1s. 6d.** net. Part III, 100 pp., **1s.** net.

Counting House Mathematics. By H. W. Porritt and W. Nicklin, A.S.A.A. In crown 8vo, cloth, 120 pp. . . . . **1s. 6d.** net.

Logarithms for Business Purposes. By H. W. Porritt and W. Nicklin, A.S.A.A. In crown 8vo, limp cloth . . . . **6d.** net.

Rapid Methods in Arithmetic. By John Johnston. In crown 8vo, cloth, 87 pp. . . **1s.** net.

Exercises in Rapid Methods in Arithmetic. By John Johnston. In crown 8vo, cloth . . **8d.** net.

Method in Arithmetic. A guide to the teaching of Arithmetic. By G. R. Purdie, B.A. In crown 8vo, cloth, 87 pp. . . . . **1s. 6d.**

Method Arithmetic. In crown 8vo, cloth, 324 pp. . . . . **3s.**

Answers to Method Arithmetic. 67 pp. . . . . **2s. 6d.** net.

Civil Service and Commercial Long and Cross Tots. In crown 8vo, 48 pp. . . . . **6d.**

Pitman's Civil Service Arithmetic Tests. By P. J. Varley-Tipton. In crown 8vo, cloth, 102 pp. . . . . **1s.** net.

BOOK-KEEPING AND ACCOUNTANCY

First Steps in Book-keeping. By W. A. Hatchard, A.C.P., F.B.T. In crown 8vo, limp cloth, 80 pp. .... **8d. net.**

Pitman's Primer of Book-keeping. Thoroughly prepares the student for the study of more elaborate treatises. In crown 8vo, cloth, 144 pp. .... **1s.**

Answers to Pitman's Primer of Book-keeping. In crown 8vo, cloth .... **1s.**

Easy Exercises for Pitman's Primer of Book-keeping. In crown 8vo, 48 pp. .... **6d.**

Book-keeping Simplified. New Edition, enlarged, and thoroughly revised. With new chapters on "Reserves" and "The Formation of Joint-Stock Companies," by W. O. Buxton, A.C.A. (Hons.). In crown 8vo, cloth, 300 pp. .... **2s. 6d.**

Answers to Book-keeping Simplified. Revised Edition. In crown 8vo, cloth .... **1s.**

Pitman's Advanced Book-keeping. In crown 8vo, cloth, 187 pp. .... **2s. 6d.**

Answers to Pitman's Advanced Book-keeping. In crown 8vo, cloth .... **1s.**

Pitman's Higher Book-keeping and Accounts. By H. W. Porritt and W. Nicklin, A.S.A.A. In crown 8vo, cloth, 304 pp., with many up-to-date forms, and facsimile documents **2s. 6d.**

Full Course in Book-keeping. By H. W. Porritt and W. Nicklin, A.S.A.A. This volume consists of the popular text-book "Higher Book-keeping and Accounts," to which has been prefixed a section on elementary Book-keeping. In crown 8vo, cloth gilt, 520 pp. **3s. 6d. net.**

Pitman's Complete Book-keeping. A thoroughly comprehensive text-book, dealing with all departments of the subject, and embracing practically every kind of account. With about 20 facsimiles of Company Forms, etc. Enlarged Edition. In crown 8vo, cloth, 424 pp. .... **3s. 6d.**

Answers to Pitman's Complete Book-keeping. Enlarged Edition. In crown 8vo, cloth, 213 pp. .... **2s. 6d.**

Book-keeping for Retailers. By H. W. Porritt and W. Nicklin, A.S.A.A. In crown 8vo, cloth, 124 pp. .... **1s. net.**

Additional Exercises in Book-keeping, Nos. I and II. New Editions. In crown 8vo, 56 pp. Each .... **6d. net.**

Answers to the Above Exercises. Nos. I and II. New Editions. Each .... **6d. net.**

Pitman's Book-keeping Test Cards. Per set .... **1s. 6d.**

Pitman's Business Book-keeping Transactions. No. I. .... **1s.**

Pitman's Book-keeping Transactions. No. II. .... **2s.**

How to Post the Ledger (Book-keeping Diagrams). By James McKee. In crown 8vo, 36 pp. **6d.**

Pitman's Hotel Book-keeping. With illustrative forms and exercises. In crown 8vo, cloth, 72 pp. .... **2s. 6d.**

How to Teach Book-keeping. By H. W. Porritt and W. Nicklin, A.S.A.A. In crown 8vo, cloth, 180 pp. .... **2s. 6d. net.**

Pitman's Examination Notes on Book-keeping and Accountancy. By J. Blake Harrold, A.C.I.S., F.C.R.A., Lecturer in Accountancy at the Birkbeck College, London. Cloth, 6½ in. by 3½ in. .... **1s. net.**

Pitman's Combined Manuscript Book for Book-keeping. In crown 4to, stiff paper wrapper, 96 pp. .... **6d.**

Ideal Manuscript Books for Book-keeping. Specially ruled and adapted for working the exercises contained in the Primer of Book-keeping. The sets consist of:—Cash Book and Journal; Purchase Book; Sales Book; Ledger. Each .... **2d.**

Avon Exercise Books for Book-keeping. Specially adapted for the exercises in "Book-keeping Simplified" or "Advanced Book-keeping." Fcap. folio. Journal, **3d.**; Cash Book, **3d.**; Ledger, **6d.**

Double Entry in One Lesson. By R. Fleming, A.C.I.S. .... **6d.**

Examination Notes on Municipal Accountancy. By W. G. Davis, A.S.A.A. Size 6½ in. by 3½ in., cloth, 56 pp. .... **1s. net.**

Balance Sheets. How to Read and Understand Them. By Philip Tovey, A.C.I.S. A complete Guide for Investors, Business Men, Commercial Students, etc. In foolscap 8vo, cloth, 85 pp. .... **1s. net.**

How to Become a Qualified Accountant. By R. A. Witty, A.S.A.A. Second Edition. In crown 8vo, cloth, 120 pp. .... **2s. net.**

Accountancy. By F. W. Pixley, F.C.A., Barrister-at-Law. In demy 8vo, cloth, 318 pp. **5s. net.**

Auditing, Accounting and Banking. By Frank Dowler, A.C.A., and E. Mardinor Harris, Associate of the Institute of Bankers. In demy 8vo, cloth gilt, 328 pp. .... **5s. net.**

The Accounts of Executors, Administrators and Trustees. By William B. Phillips, A.C.A. (Hons. Inter. and Final), A.C.I.S., Lecturer on the subject to the Manchester Evening School of Commerce, and late Lecturer to the Manchester Chartered Accountants' Students' Society. In demy 8vo, cloth gilt .... **3s. 6d. net.**

Gold Mine Accounts and Costing. A Practical Manual for Officials, Accountants, Book-keepers, Etc. By G. W. Tait, of the South African staff of a leading group of mines. In demy 8vo, cloth gilt, 93 pp. .... **5s. net.**

Income Tax Accounts and How to Prepare Them. Notes on Income Tax Law and Practice. In crown 8vo, cloth .... **2s.**

The Farmer's Account Book. Compiled by W. G. Dowsley, B.A. A Simple and concise System of Account Keeping specially adapted to the requirements of Farmers. Size, 15½ in. by 9½ in., half leather, 106 pp., with interleaved blotting paper .... **6s. 6d. net.**

The Personal Account Book. By the same author. Size, 15½ in. by 9½ in., half leather, 106 pp., with interleaved blotting paper .... **6s. 6d. net.**

BUSINESS TRAINING

Office Routine for Boys and Girls, 1st Stage. In crown 8vo, 64 pp. .... **6d.**

Office Routine for Boys and Girls, 2nd Stage. In crown 8vo, 64 pp. .... **6d.**

Office Routine for Boys and Girls, 3rd Stage. In crown 8vo, 64 pp. .... **6d.**

First Steps in Business Training. By V. E. Collinge, A.C.I.S. In crown 8vo, limp cloth, 80 pp. .... **8d. net.**

Counting-House Routine. 1st Year's Course. By Vincent E. Collinge, A.C.I.S. New Edition, thoroughly Revised and Enlarged. In crown 8vo, cloth, with illustrations, maps, and facsimile commercial forms, 162 pp. .... **1s. net.**

Counting-House Routine. 2nd Year's Course. By Vincent E. Collinge, A.C.I.S. New Edition, thoroughly Revised and Enlarged. In crown 8vo, cloth, with illustrations, maps, and facsimile commercial forms, 188 pp. .... **1s. 6d. net.**

Pitman's Manual of Business Training. Contains 57 maps and facsimiles. Seventh Edition, thoroughly revised and considerably enlarged. In crown 8vo, cloth, 282 pp..... **2s. 6d.**

The Theory and Practice of Commerce. Being a Complete Guide to Methods and Machinery of Business. Edited by F. Heelis, F.C.I.S., Examiner in Business Training to the Lancashire and Cheshire Union of Institutes, the West Riding County Council, and the Midland Union of Institutes. Assisted by Specialist Contributors. In demy 8vo, cloth gilt, 620 pp., with many facsimile forms. **4s. 6d.** net. Also in 2 vols, each price **2s. 6d.** net.

Guide to Business Customs and Practice on the Continent. By Emil Davies. In crown 8vo, cloth, 154 pp. .... **2s. 6d.** net.

How to Get a Situation Abroad. By Emil Davies. In crown 8vo, cloth........ **1s. 6d.** net.

Masters' New Ready Reckoner. Pitman's Edition. Contains 63,000 calculations. In foolscap 8vo, cloth, 358 pp. .... **1s.** net.

Pitman's Discount, Commission, and Brokerage Tables. By Ernest Heavingham. Size 3 in. by 4¾ in., cloth, 160 pp., ... **1s.** net.

How to Start in Life. By A. Kingston. A Popular Guide to Commercial, Municipal, Civil Service, and Professional Employment. Deals with over 70 distinct kinds of Employment. In crown 8vo, cloth, 128 pp. .... **1s. 6d.**

Guide to the Mercantile Marine. By R. A. Fletcher. A Guide to all who wish to join it. With illustrations. In crown 8vo, cloth .... **1s. 6d.** net.

The Junior Corporation Clerk. By J. B. Carrington, F.S.A.A., Borough Accountant of Paddington; Member of the Institute of Municipal Treasurers and Accountants (Incorporated): etc., etc. In crown 8vo, cloth gilt, with illustrations........ **1s. 6d.** net.

Pitman's Business Terms, Phrases and Abbreviations. Fourth Edition, revised and enlarged. In crown 8vo, cloth, 280 pp. .... **2s. 6d.** net.

Mercantile Terms and Abbreviations. Containing over 1,000 terms and 500 abbreviations used in commerce, with definitions. Size 3 in. by 4¾ in., cloth 126 pp.,........ **1s.** net.

Commercial Terms in Five Languages. Being about 1,900 terms and phrases used in commerce, with their equivalents in French, German, Spanish, and Italian. Size 3 in. by 4¾ in., cloth, 118 pp. .... **1s.** net.

How to Teach Business Training. By F. Heelis, F.C.I.S. In crown 8vo, 160 pp... **2s. 6d.** net.

Questions in Business Training. By F. Heelis, F.C.I.S. In crown 8vo, cloth, 108 pp..... **1s.**

Answers to Questions in Business Training. By the same author. In crown 8vo, cloth, about 160 pp. .... **2s.**

Questions and Answers in Business Training. By the same author. In crown 8vo, cloth, 269 pp. .... **2s. 6d.**

Business Methods and Secretarial Work for Girls and Women. By Helene Reinherz, M.A., Junior Bursar, Girton College, Cambridge. In crown 8vo, cloth, 96 pp......... **1s.** net.

Digesting Returns into Summaries. By A. J. Lawford Jones, of H.M. Civil Service. In crown 8vo, cloth, 84 pp. .... **1s. 6d.** net.

Pitman's Civil Service Guide. By A. J. Lawford Jones. In crown 8vo, cloth, 100 pp. **1s.** net.

Copying Manuscript, Orthography, Handwriting, etc. By the same author. Actual Examination Papers only. In foolscap 4to, 48 pp. ....**2s.** net.
Clerks : Their Rights and Obligations. By Edward A. Cope. In foolscap 8vo, cloth, 160 pp. **1s.** net.
Handbook for Commercial Teachers. By Fred Hall, M.A., B.Com., F.C.I.S., etc. ; Professor of Commerce and Head of the Department of Commerce, Municipal Technical Institute, Belfast ; and formerly Lecturer in Commercial Subjects to the Rochdale, Bury, and Salford Education Committees. In crown 8vo, cloth gilt, 200 pp. ....**2s. 6d.** net.

COMMERCIAL CORRESPONDENCE AND ENGLISH

First Steps in Commercial English. By W. Jayne Weston, M.A. (Lond.) , B.Sc. (Lond.). In crown 8vo, limp cloth, 80 pp...**8d.** net.
Pitman's Guide to Commercial Correspondence and Business Composition. By W. Jayne Weston, M.A. Cloth, 146 pp., with many facsimile commercial documents ....**1s. 6d.**
Manual of Commercial English. By Walter Shawcross, B.A. Including Composition and Précis Writing. In crown 8vo, cloth gilt, 234 pp. ....**2s. 6d.** net.
Pitman's Commercial Correspondence and Commercial English. In crown 8vo, cloth, 272 pp. ....**2s. 6d.**
How to Teach Commercial English. By Walter Shawcross, B.A. In crown 8vo, cloth gilt, 160 pp. ....**2s. 6d.** net.
Pitman's International Mercantile Letters. In five volumes, crown 8vo, cloth gilt, each about 250 pp. **English-German, 2s. 6d. English, 2s. 6d. English-French, 2s. 6d. English-Italian, 3s. English-Portuguese, 3s. 6d.**.
Pitman's Dictionary of Commercial Correspondence in French, German, Spanish, and Italian. Second, Revised and Cheaper Edition. In demy 8vo, cloth, 502 pp. ....**5s.** net.
Punctuation as a Means of Expression. By A. E. Lovell, M.A. In crown 8vo, cloth, 80 pp. **1s. 6d.**
The Avon English Grammar Primer. Cloth, 219 pp. ....**1s.**
English Grammar. New Edition, Revised and Enlarged by C. D. Punchard, B.A. (Lond.). In crown 8vo, cloth, 142 pp. ....**1s.** net.
A Guide to English Composition. By the Rev. J. H. Bacon. 112 pp., paper **1s.** ; cloth, **1s. 6d.**
Notes of Lessons on English. In crown 8vo, cloth 208 pp...........................**3s. 6d.**
Grammar and its Reasons : For Students and Teachers of the English Tongue. By Mary Holland Leonard. In crown 8vo, cloth, 392 pp...............................**3s. 6d.** net.
Pitman's Studies in Elocution. By E. M. Corbould (*Mrs. Mark Robinson*). With over 100 selections for Reciters and Readers. In crown 8vo, cloth gilt, gilt top ....**2s. 6d.** net.
English Composition and Correspondence. By J. F. Davis, D.Lit., M.A., LL.B. (Lond.). In crown 8vo, cloth, 118 pp...**1s.** net.
The Foreign Correspondent. By Emil Davies. In crown 8vo, cloth, 80 pp.......**1s. 6d.** net.
Pitman's Pocket Dictionary. Royal 32mo, 5 in. by 3 in., cloth gilt, 362 pp., **1s.** net ; also in leather, **1s. 6d.** net.
Commercial Dictionary. In crown 8vo, paper boards, **9d.** net. ; cloth .... **1s.** net.
Studies in Essay Writing. By V. P. Peacock. In crown 8vo, paper, **6d.** net., cloth **9d.** net.
Guide to Indexing and Précis Writing. By William Jayne Weston, M.A., and E. Bowker. In crown 8vo, cloth, 110 pp. ....**1s.** net.
Indexing and Précis Writing. By A. J. Lawford Jones, of H.M. Civil Service, Medallist and First Prizeman, Society of Arts, 1900. In crown 8vo, cloth, 144 pp...........**1s. 6d.**
Exercises and Answers in Indexing and Précis Writing. By Wm. Jayne Weston, M.A. (Lond.). In crown 8vo, cloth, 144 pp. ....**1s. 6d.**

COMMERCIAL GEOGRAPHY

First Steps in Commercial Geography. By James Stephenson, M.A., B.Com. There are 16 maps and diagrams included. In crown 8vo, limp cloth, 80 pp. ....**8d.** net.
The World and its Commerce. In crown 8vo, cloth, 128 pp., with 34 maps................**1s.**
Pitman's Commercial Geography of the British Isles. New Edition, Revised and Enlarged. In crown 8vo, cloth, 150 pp., with 34 coloured maps and plates, three black and white maps, and other illustrations ....**1s.**

Pitman's Commercial Geography of the British Empire Abroad and Foreign Countries. New Edition, Revised and Enlarged. In crown 8vo, cloth, 205 pp., with 35 coloured maps and plates, 11 black and white maps, and end-paper maps............**1s. 6d.**
Pitman's Commercial Geography of the World. New Edition, Revised and Enlarged. In crown 8vo, cloth, 350 pp., with about 90 maps and plates..........**2s. 6d.**
Examination Notes on Commercial Geography. By W. P. Rutter, M.Com. Size 6½ in. by 3½ in., cloth, 120 pp..............**1s. 6d.** net.

COMMERCIAL HISTORY

Commercial History. By J. R. V. Marchant, M.A., formerly Scholar of Wadham College, Oxford, Examiner in Commercial History to the London Chamber of Commerce. In crown 8vo, cloth gilt, 272 pp..............**3s.**
Pitman's Industrial and Social History. By George Collar, B.A., B.Sc. (Lond.). In crown 8vo, cloth, with over 100 illustrations, 284 pp..............**2s.**

COMMERCIAL READERS

Pitman's Commercial Reader (Intermediate Book). In crown 8vo, cloth, 240 pp. Illustrated..............**1s. 9d.**
Pitman's Commercial Reader (Senior Book). An Introduction to Modern Commerce. Contains over 160 black and white illustrations. In crown 8vo, cloth, 272 pp.........**2s.**

FRENCH

A Child's First Steps in French. By A. Vizetelly. An elementary French reader with vocabulary. Illustrated. In crown 8vo, limp cloth..............**9d.**
Pitman's French Course, Part I. In crown 8vo, paper, **6d.**; cloth..............**8d.**
Pitman's French Course, Part II. In crown 8vo, paper, **8d.**; cloth..............**10d.**
Key to Pitman's French Course, Parts I and II. In crown 8vo, each..............**1s. 6d.**
Pitman's Practical French Grammar. With copious Vocabulary and Imitated Pronunciation. In crown 8vo, 120 pp., paper, **1s.**; cloth..............**1s. 6d.**
Pitman's Commercial French Grammar. By F. W. M. Draper, B.A., B. ès L. Of Queens' College, Cambridge, and Licencié of the University of Paris; also Assistant Master at the City of London School. In crown 8vo, cloth gilt, 166 pp..............**2s. 6d.** net.
French Business Letters. First Series. In crown 4to..............**6d.** net.
French Business Letters. By A. H. Bernaardt. Second Series. In crown 8vo.......**6d.** net.
Commercial Correspondence in French. In crown 8vo, cloth, 240 pp..........**2s. 6d.**
French Commercial Reader. In crown 8vo, cloth, 208 pp..............**2s. 6d.**
French Commercial Phrases and Abbreviations with Translation. In crown 8vo........**6d.**
French Business Interviews. In crown 8vo, 80 pp., paper, **1s.**; cloth..........**1s. 6d.**
Easy French Conversational Sentences. In crown 8vo..............**6d.**
Advanced French Conversational Exercises. In crown 8vo..............**6d.**
Examinations in French, and How to Pass Them. In crown 8vo..............**6d.**
Examination Notes on French. By F. W. M. Draper. Size 6½ in. by 3½ in., cloth, 50 pp. **1s.** net.
Tourists' Vade Mecum of French Colloquial Conversation. Handy size for the pocket, cloth, **1s.** net.
French Translation and Composition. By Lewis Marsh, B.A. (Hons.), Cantab., Med. and Mod. Languages Tripos, Late Exhibitioner of Emmanual College; White Prizeman; Assistant Master, City of London School; and Special Instructor in French and German to the London County Council. In crown 8vo, cloth, 187 pp..............**2s. 6d.**
French Prose Writers of the XIXth Century and After. By Victor Leuliette, B. ès L., A.K.C. An advanced French Reader with Biographical and Critical Notices in French and Literary and Bibliographical Notes in English. In crown 8vo, cloth gilt, 350 pp...**3s.** net.
French Phrases for Advanced Students. By Edward J. Kealey, B.A., formerly Classical and Modern Languages Master at Ampleforth College, York; late Senior French Master to the Grammar School, Dudley; and County Council Instructor at the Municipal Technical School, Wednesbury. New, Revised and Enlarged Edition. In crown 8vo, cloth, 140 pp..............**1s. 6d.** net.

Pitman's International Mercantile Letters. English-French. In crown 8vo, cloth..**2s. 6d.**
English-French and French-English Dictionary of Business Words and Terms. Size 2 in. by 6 in., cloth, rounded corners ....**2s. 6d.** net.
Le Bourgeois Gentilhomme. Molière's Comedy in French, fully annotated...**1s.**; cloth, **1s. 6d.**
Vest Pocket List of Endings of French Regular and Auxiliary Verbs. With notes on the Participles and the Infinitive. Size 2¾ in. by 1¾ in. 48 pp. ....**2d.** net.

GERMAN

Pitman's German Course. Part I. In crown 8vo, paper, **6d.**; cloth ....**8d.**
Key to Pitman's German Course. Part I. In crown 8vo..............................**1s. 6d.**
Pitman's Practical German Grammar. In crown 8vo, paper, **1s.**; cloth .... **1s. 6d.**
Pitman's Commercial German Grammar. By J. Bithell, M.A., Lecturer in German at the Birkbeck College, London; Recognised Teacher of the University of London. In crown 8vo, cloth gilt ....**2s. 6d.** net.
German Business Interviews, Nos. 1 and 2. In crown 8vo, paper, **1s.**; cloth .... **1s. 6d.**
Elementary German Correspondence. By Lewis Marsh, M.A. In crown 8vo, cloth......**2s.**
Commercial Correspondence in German. In crown 8vo, cloth, 240 pp..................**2s. 6d.**
German Commercial Reader. In crown 8vo, cloth, 208 pp. ....**2s. 6d.**
German Business Letters. First Series. In crown 8vo......................................**6d.** net.
German Business Letters. By G. Albers. Second Series. In crown 8vo..............**6d.** net.
German Commercial Phrases. In crown 8vo ....**6d.**
German Examination Papers with Model Answers. In crown 8vo...........................**6d.**
Examination Notes on German. By A. Hargreaves, M.A., Ph.D., Modern Language Master at the City of London School. Cloth, 6½ in. by 3½ in., 56 pp..........................**1s.** net.
Easy German Conversational Sentences. In crown 8vo...**6d.**
Advanced German Conversational Exercises. In crown 8vo......................................**6d.**
Tourists' Vade Mecum of German Colloquial Conversation. In crown 8vo, cloth......**1s.** net.
Der Neffe Als Onkel. Schiller's Comedy, fully annotated. In crown 8vo, paper, **6d.**; cloth, **1s.**
English-German and German-English Dictionary of Business Words and Terms. Size 2 in. by 6 in., rounded corners, cloth ....**2s. 6d.** net.
Pitman's International Mercantile Letters. English-German. In crown 8vo, cloth..**2s. 6d.**

ITALIAN

Tourists' Vade Mecum of Italian Colloquial Conversation. Cloth ....**1s.** net.
International Mercantile Letters. English-Italian. In crown 8vo, cloth.....................**3s.**
Italian Business Letters. By A. Valgimigli. In crown 8vo. ....**6d.** net.
Pitman's Italian Commercial Grammar. By Luigi Ricci, Professor at the University of London. In crown 8vo, cloth gilt...**2s. 6d.** net.

SPANISH AND PORTUGUESE

Spanish Business Letters. First Series. In crown 8vo ....**6d.** net.
Spanish Business Letters. By E. McConnell. 2nd Series. In crown 8vo, 48 pp.....**6d.** net.
Spanish Business Interviews. With Correspondence, Invoices, etc. In crown 8vo, paper, **1s.**; cloth. **1s. 6d.**
Easy Spanish Conversational Sentences. In crown 8vo...**6d.**
Advanced Spanish Conversational Exercises. In crown 8vo ....**6d.**
Pitman's Practical Spanish Grammar. In crown 8vo, paper, **1s.**; cloth .... **1s. 6d.**
Pitman's Spanish Commercial Grammar. By C. A. Toledano, Spanish Master at the Manchester Municipal School of Commerce, Manchester Athenæum, etc. In crown 8vo, cloth gilt, 250 pp. ....**2s. 6d.** net.
Spanish Commercial Phrases. With abbreviations and translation. In crown 8vo ......**8d.**
Examination Notes on Spanish. By Alfred Calvert, Public Translator of European Languages; Lecturer in French, German, Spanish, etc., etc., at the Manchester Municipal School of Commerce. Cloth, 6½ in. by 3½ in., 56 pp. ....**1s.** net.
Tourists' Vade Mecum of Spanish Colloquial Conversation. Cloth ....**1s.** net.
Commercial Correspondence in Spanish. In crown 8vo, cloth, 240 pp...................**2s. 6d.**
A New Dictionary of the Portuguese and English Languages. In two vols., each **15s.** net.
Abridged Edition, two parts in one vol., ...**15s.** net.
Pitman's International Mercantile Letters. English-Portuguese. In crown 8vo, cloth. **3s. 6d.**

HANDWRITING, Etc.

Pitman's Commercial Handwriting and Correspondence. In foolscap 4to, quarter cloth. **2s.**

Business Handwriting. Seventh Edition, Revised. In crown 8vo, cloth, 84 pp. .... **1s.**

Pitman's Commercial Copy and Exercise Books. In foolscap folio, 32 pp., each .... **6d.**

First Steps in Business Letter Writing. By Fred. Hall, M.A., B.Com., F.C.I.S., etc. In crown 8vo, cloth, about 80 pp. .... **8d.** net.

Pitman's "New Era" Business Copy Books. By F. Heelis, F.C.I.S. Civil Service Style. In three books, Junior, Intermediate, and Senior. Each in stout paper covers, large post 4to, 32 pp. .... **4d.**

Exercise Books of Facsimile Commercial Forms. In large post 4to, printed in red and black, in wrapper, 32 pp. .... **6d.**

Pitman's Facsimile Commercial Forms. New, Revised, and Enlarged Edition. 35 separate forms in envelope, **6d.** net. Forms separately, per doz., **3d.**

Pitman's Office Routine Copy Book, No. 1. In large post 4to, 24 pp. .... **3d.**

Pitman's Office Routine Copy Book, No. 2. In large post 4to, 24 pp. .... **3d.**

Pitman's Office Routine Copy Book, No. 3. In large post 4to, 24 pp. .... **3d.**

Civil Service and Commercial Copying Forms. In crown 8vo, 40 pp. .... **6d.**

Ruled Forms for use with the above. Books I and II. Each foolscap folio, 40 pp. .... **8d.**

COMMON COMMODITIES OF COMMERCE SERIES

Each book in crown 8vo, cloth, with coloured frontispiece and many illustrations, maps, charts, etc. **1s. 6d.** net.

Tea. From Grower to Consumer. By A. Ibbetson. Of Messrs. Joseph Travers & Sons.

Coffee. From Grower to Consumer. By B. B. Keable. Of Messrs. Joseph Travers & Sons.

Cotton. From the Raw Material to the Finished Product. By R. J. Peake.

Sugar, Cane and Beet. By Geo. Martineau, C.B.

Oil, Animal, Vegetable, Essential, and Mineral. By C. Ainsworth Mitchell.

Rubber. Production and Utilisation of the Raw Product. By C. Beadle and H. P. Stevens, M.A., Ph.D., F.I.C.

Iron and Steel. Their Production and Manufacture. By C. Hood, of the well-known firm of Messrs. Bell Brothers, Limited.

Silk. Its Production and Manufacture. By Luther Hooper. Weaver, Designer, and Manufacturer.

Tobacco. From Grower to Smoker. By A. E. Tanner, Chemical Officer in the Customs and Excise Department.

Wool. From the Raw Material to the Finished Product. By J. A. Hunter.

Coal. Its Origin, Method of Working, and Preparation for the Market. By Francis H. Wilson, M.Inst., M.E., Editor of "Mining Engineering"; Lecturer on Mining at the Leigh Technical School.

Other volumes in preparation.

PRACTICAL PRIMERS OF BUSINESS

Each in crown 8vo, cloth, about 120 pp., **1s.** net.

The Money, and the Stock and Share Markets. By Emil Davies.

Shipping. By Arnold Hall and F. Heywood.

The Elements of Banking. By J. P. Gandy.

The Elements of Insurance. By J. Alfred Eke.

Advertising. By Howard Bridgewater.

The Card Index System. Its Principles, Uses, Operation, and Component Parts. By R. B. Byles.

Book-keeping for Retailers. By H. W. Porritt, and W. Nicklin, A.S.A.A.

The Elements of Commercial Law. By A. H. Douglas, LL.B.

English Composition and Correspondence. By J. F. Davis, M.A., D.Litt., LL.B.

Guide to Indexing and Précis Writing. By W. J. Weston, M.A., and E. Bowker.

BUSINESS HANDBOOKS

Pitman's Commercial Encyclopædia and Dictionary of Business. Edited by J. A. Slater, B.A., LL.B. (Lond.). Of the Middle Temple and North-Eastern Circuit, Barrister-at-Law. Assisted by upwards of 50 specialists as contributors. A reliable and comprehensive work of reference on all commercial subjects, specially designed and written for the busy merchant, the commercial student, and the modern man of affairs. With numerous maps, illustrations, facsimile business forms and legal documents, diagrams, etc. Orders for complete sets only of the work can be accepted. An elaborate prospectus, containing full particulars with specimen pages, forms, maps, etc., has been prepared, and will be sent post free on application. In 4 vols., large crown 4to (each about 450 pp.), cloth gilt, **£1 10s.** net. Half leather gilt, **£2 2s.** net.

Pitman's Business Man's Guide. Edited by J. A. Slater, B.A., LL.B. Fifth Edition, Revised. In crown 8vo, cloth cover of special design, 500 pp. .... **3s. 6d.** net.

Pitman's Public Man's Guide. Edited by J. A. Slater, B.A., LL.B. (Lond.). A Handbook for all who take an interest in questions of the day. In crown 8vo, cloth gilt, 444 pp. **3s. 6d.** net.

Lectures on British Commerce, including Finance, Insurance, Business and Industry. By the Rt. Hon. Frederick Huth Jackson, G. Armitage-Smith, M.A., D.Litt., Robert Bruce, C.B., etc. In demy 8vo, cloth gilt, 295 pp. .... **7s. 6d.** net.

Office Organisation and Management, Including Secretarial Work. By Lawrence R. Dicksee, M.Com. F.C.A., and H. E. Blain, Tramways Manager, County Borough of West Ham. New Edition, Revised. In demy 8vo, cloth gilt, 306 pp. .... **5s.** net.

Counting-House and Factory Organisation. By J. Gilmour Williamson, Holder of Business, Diploma of the Heriot-Watt College, Edinburgh. In demy 8vo, cloth gilt, 182 pp. **5s.** net.

Insurance. By T. E. Young, B.A., F.R.A.S., ex-President of the Institute of Actuaries; ex-Chairman of the Life Offices' Association, etc., etc. A complete and practical exposition for the Student and the Business Man. Second Edition. In demy 8vo, cloth gilt, 408 pp. .... **5s.** net.

Insurance Office Organisation, Management, and Accounts. By T. E. Young, B.A., F.R.A.S., and Richard Masters, A.C.A. Second Edition, Revised. In demy 8vo, cloth gilt, 146 pp. .... **3s. 6d.** net.

Shipping Office Organisation, Management, and Accounts. By Alfred Calvert. In demy 8vo, cloth gilt, 203 pp. .... **5s.** net.

Solicitors' Office Organisation, Management, and Accounts. By E. A. Cope, and H. W. H. Robins. In demy 8vo, cloth gilt, 176 pp., with numerous forms .... **5s.** net.

Stockbrokers' Office Organisation, Management, and Accounts. By J. E. Day, Managing Clerk to a London firm of Inside brokers. In demy 8vo, cloth gilt, 242 pp... **7s. 6d.** net.

Drapery Business Organisation, Management and Accounts. By J. Ernest Bayley. In demy 8vo, cloth gilt .... **5s.** net.

Grocery Business Organisation and Management. By C. L. T. Beeching, Secretary and Fellow of the Institute of Certificated Grocers. **With Chapters on Buying a Business, Grocers' Office Work and Book-keeping, and a Model Set of Grocer's Accounts.** By J. Arthur Smart, of the Firm of Alfred Smart, Valuer and Accountant; Fellow of the Institute of Certificated Grocers. In demy 8vo, cloth gilt, about 160 pp., with illustrations **5s.** net.

Bank Organisation, Management, and Accounts. By J. F. Davis, M.A., D.Lit., LL.B. (Lond.), Lecturer in Banking and Finance at the City of London College. In demy 8vo, cloth gilt, 165 pp., with forms .... **5s.** net.

Dictionary of Banking. A Complete Encyclopædia of Banking Law and Practice. By W. Thomson, Bank Inspector. In crown 4to, half leather gilt, about 550 pp..... **21s.** net.

Money, Exchange, and Banking. In their Practical, Theoretical, and Legal Aspects. By H. T. Easton, of the Union of London and Smiths Bank, Ltd. Second Edition, Revised. In demy 8vo, cloth, 312 pp. .... **5s.** net.

Practical Banking (including Currency). By J. F. G. Bagshaw, Fourth Gilbart Prizeman, Author of "Bank Balance Sheets and How to Prepare Them," etc., and C. F. Hannaford, Associate of the Institute of Bankers, Examiner in Banking and Currency to the London Chamber of Commerce. In demy 8vo, cloth gilt, 320 pp. .... **5s.** net.

Bank Balance Sheets and How to Prepare Them. By J. F. G. Bagshaw. In demy 8vo, **6d.** net.

The History, Law, and Practice of the Stock Exchange. By A. P. Poley, B.A., Barrister-at-Law, and F. H. Carruthers Gould, of the Stock Exchange. Second Edition, Revised. In demy 8vo, cloth gilt, 348 pp. .... **5s.** net.

The Students' Guide to Marine Insurance. By Henry Keate, Lecturer on Marine Insurance at the Manchester School of Commerce. In crown 8vo, cloth gilt, 203 pp.... **2s. 6d.** net,

The Student's Guide to Company Secretarial Work. By O. Oldham, A.C.I.S. In crown 8vo. cloth gilt, 256 pp. .... **2s. 6d.** net.

The Company Secretary's Vade Mecum. In foolscap 8vo, cloth, 183 pp. .... **1s. 6d.** net.
Pitman's Guide for the Company Secretary. By Arthur Coles, A.C.I.S., Sometime Lecturer in the Technological Schools of the London County Council. With an Introduction by Herbert E. Blain. Illustrated with 54 facsimile forms. In demy 8vo, cloth gilt, 346 pp. **5s.** net.
The Chairman's Manual. By Gurdon Palin, of Gray's Inn, Barrister-at-Law, and Ernest Martin, F.C.I.S. In crown 8vo, cloth gilt, 192 pp. .... **2s. 6d.** net.
Prospectuses. How to Read and Understand Them. By Philip Tovey, A.C.I.S. In demy 8vo, cloth gilt, 109 pp. .... **1s. 6d.** net.
Pitman's Secretary's Handbook. Edited by Herbert E. Blain. In demy 8vo, cloth gilt, 168 pp. .... **3s. 6d.** net.
The Transfer of Stocks, Shares, and Other Marketable Securities. A Manual of the Law and Practice. By F. D. Head, B.A. (Oxon.), late Classical Exhibitioner of Queen's College; of Lincoln's Inn, Barrister-at-Law. Second Edition, Revised and enlarged. In demy 8vo, cloth gilt, 220 pp. .... **5s.** net.
How to Take Minutes. In demy 8vo, cloth, 80 pp. .... **1s. 6d.** net.
Cost Accounts in Principle and Practice. By A. Clifford Ridgway, A.C.A. In demy 8vo, cloth gilt, 120 pp. .... **3s. 6d.** net.
The Trader's Guide to County Court Procedure. By F. H. B. Chapman. In foolscap 8vo, cloth 112 pp. .... **1s.** net.
Salesmanship. By W. A. Corbion and G. E. Grimsdale. In crown 8vo, cloth, 186 pp. **2s. 6d.** net.
Advertising. By Howard Bridgewater .... **1s.** net
Handbook of Advertising. By Christopher Jones. In crown 8vo, cloth gilt ...... **2s. 6d.** net.
The Theory and Practice of Advertising. By Walter Dill Scott, Ph.D., Director of the Psychological Laboratory of North-Western University, U.S.A. In large crown 8vo, cloth, with 61 illustrations, 240 pp. .... **6s.** net.
The Psychology of Advertising. By the same author. In large crown 8vo, cloth gilt, with 67 illustrations, 282 pp. .... **6s.** net.
The Principles of Practical Publicity. Being a Treatise on "The Art of Advertising." By Truman A. de Weese. In large crown 8vo, cloth, with 43 full-page illustrations, 266 pp. **7s. 6d.** net.
Ads and Sales. A Study of Advertising and Selling from the Standpoint of the New Principles of Scientific Management. By Herbert N. Casson. In demy 8vo, cloth, 167 pp. **6s.** net.
PITMAN'S TRADER'S HANDBOOKS. In crown 8vo, cloth, 260 pp. **2s. 6d.** net.
- **Drapery and Drapers' Accounts.** By Richard Beynon.
- **Grocery and Grocers' Accounts.** By W. F. Tupman.
- **Ironmongery and Ironmongers' Accounts.** By S. W. Francis.

The World's Commercial Products. By W. G. Freeman, B.Sc., F.L.S., Superintendent, Colonial Economic Collections, Imperial Institute, London, and S. E. Chandler, D.Sc., F.L.S., Assistant, Colonial Economic Collections, Imperial Institute, London. With contributions by numerous Specialists. In demy 4to, cloth gilt, with 12 coloured plates, 12 maps, and 420 illustrations from photographs. 432 pp. .... **10s. 6d.** net.
Dictionary of the World's Commercial Products. By J. A. Slater, B.A. LL.B. (Lond.). Second Edition, Revised. In demy 8vo, cloth, 163 pp. .... **2s. 6d.**
Pitman's Office Desk Book. Second, Revised and Cheaper Edition. In crown 8vo, cloth, 309 pp. .... **1s.** net.
The "Cole" Code, or Code Dictionary. Size 7½ in. by 10 in., cloth, 272 pp. .... **15s.** net.
Where to Look. In crown 8vo, cloth, 140 pp. .... **2s.** net.
Economics for Business Men. By W. J. Weston, M.A. (Lond.). B.Sc. (Lond.). In crown 8vo, cloth .... **1s. 6d.** net.
The Student's Guide to Political Economy. By F. H. Spencer, D.Sc., LL.B., Fellow of the Royal Statistical Society, and of the Royal Economic Society; Lecturer in Economics and Director of the Day Commercial School, City of London College. In crown 8vo, cloth gilt, 232 pp. .... **2s. 6d.** net.
Outlines of the Economic History of England, A Study in Social Development. By H. O. Meredith, M.A., M.Com. Fellow of King's College, Cambridge; Professor of Economics, Queen's University, Belfast; Sometime Russell Research Student and Lecturer in the London School of Economics; Sometime Lecturer in Economics at Cambridge University. In demy 8vo, cloth gilt, 376 pp. .... **5s.** net.
Systematic Indexing. By J. Kaiser In royal 8vo, cloth gilt, with 32 illustrations and 12 coloured plates .... **12s. 6d.** net.
Consular Requirements for Exporters and Shippers to all Parts of the World. By J. S. Nowery. In crown 8vo, cloth, 82 pp. .... **2s. 6d.** net.
A Complete Guide to the Improvement of the Memory. By the late Rev. J. H. Bacon. In foolscap 8vo, cloth .... **1s.** net.
How to Study and Remember. By B. J. Davies. Third Edition. In crown 8vo .... **6d.** net.

LAW

The Elements of Commercial Law. By A. H. Douglas, LL.B. (Lond.). In crown 8vo, cloth, 128 pp. .... **1s. net.**

The Commercial Law of England. By J. A. Slater, B.A., LL.B. (Lond.). In crown 8vo, cloth, 227 pp. Fifth Edition. .... **2s. 6d.**

Questions and Answers in Commercial Law. By J. Wells Thatcher, Barrister-at-Law. In crown 8vo, cloth, gilt .... **2s. 6d.**

Examination Notes on Commercial Law. By R. W. Holland, M.A., M.Sc., LL.B., Barrister-at-Law; Lecturer in Commercial Law at the Manchester Municipal School of Commerce. Cloth, 6½ in. by 3½ in. .... **1s. net.**

Elementary Law for Shorthand Clerks and Typists. In crown 8vo, cloth, 213 pp. .... **2s. 6d.**

Legal Terms, Phrases, and Abbreviations. In crown 8vo, cloth, 200 pp. .... **2s. 6d.**

Conveyancing. By E. A. Cope. In crown 8vo, cloth, 206 pp. .... **3s. net.**

Wills, Executors, and Trustees. With a Chapter on Intestacy. By J. A. Slater, B.A. LL.B. (Lond.). In foolscap 8vo, cloth, 122 pp. .... **1s. net.**

The Law Relating to Trade Customs, Marks, Secrets, Restraints, Agencies, etc., etc. By Lawrence Duckworth Barrister-at-Law. In foolscap 8vo, cloth, 116 pp. .... **1s. net.**

The Householders' Legal Rights and Duties with Respect to his Neighbours, the Public, and the State. By J. A. Slater, B.A., LL.B. (Lond.). In foolscap 8vo, cloth, 130 pp... **1s. net.**

The Householders' Guide to the Law with Respect to Landlord and Tenant, Husband and Wife, Parent and Child, and Master and Servant. By the same author. In foolscap 8vo, cloth, 137 pp. .... **1s. net.**

Household Law. By J. A. Slater, B.A., LL.B. (Lond.). In demy 8vo, cloth gilt, 316 pp. **5s. net.**

Pitman's Mercantile Law. By J. A. Slater, B.A., LL.B. (Lond.). In demy 8vo, cloth gilt, 448 pp. Second Edition, revised and enlarged. .... **5s. net.**

Pitman's Bills, Cheques, and Notes. In demy 8vo, cloth gilt, 206 pp. .... **2s. 6d. net.**

Income Tax and Inhabited House Duty Law and Cases. By W. E. Snelling. In demy 8vo, cloth gilt, 278 pp. .... **5s. net.**

Encyclopædia of Marine Law. By Lawrence Duckworth, Barrister-at-Law. Second Edition, Revised and Enlarged. In demy 8vo, cloth gilt, 386 pp. .... **5s. net.**

The Law of Heavy and Light Mechanical Traction on Highways in the United Kingdom. By C. A. Montague Barlow, M.P., M.A., LL.D., and W. Joynson Hicks, M.P. In demy 8vo, cloth gilt, 318 pp. .... **8s. 6d. net.**

The Student's Guide to Company Law. By R. W. Holland, M.A., M.Sc., LL.B. (Hons.). In crown 8vo, cloth gilt, 203 pp. .... **2s. 6d. net**

Companies and Company Law. Together with the Companies (Consolidation) Act, 1908. By A. C. Connell, LL.B. (Lond.). In demy 8vo, cloth gilt, 344 pp. .... **5s. net.**

The Law of Carriage. By J. E. R. Stephens, B.A. Of the Middle Temple, Barrister-at-Law. In demy 8vo, cloth gilt, 340 pp. .... **5s. net.**

The Student's Guide to Bankruptcy Law and Winding up of Companies. By F. Porter Fausset, B.A., LL.B., Barrister-at-Law. In crown 8vo, cloth gilt, 187 pp. .... **2s. 6d. net.**

Bankruptcy and Bills of Sale. An A B C of the Law. By W. Valentine Ball, M.A., Barrister-at-Law. Second Edition, Revised and Enlarged. In demy 8vo, cloth gilt, 386 pp. **5s. net.**

Farm Law. By M. G. Johnson. In demy 8vo, cloth gilt, 160 pp. .... **3s. 6d. net.**

Pitman's Guide to the Law of Licensing. The Handbook for all Licence Holders. By J. Wells Thatcher, Barrister-at-Law. In demy 8vo, cloth gilt, 196 pp. .... **5s. net.**

Law of Repairs and Dilapidations. A Handbook for Students and Practitioners. By T. Cato Worsfold, M.A., LL.D. In crown 8vo, cloth gilt, ... **3s. 6d. net.**

The Law of Contract. By R. W. Holland, M.A., M.Sc., LL.B. (Hons.). Of the Middle Temple, Barrister-at-Law. In foolscap 8vo, cloth, 120 pp. .... **1s. 6d. net.**

The Law of Evidence. A Handbook for Students and Practitioners. By W. Nembhard Hibbert, LL.D. (Lond.), Barrister-at-Law of the Middle Temple; sometime Dean of the Faculty of Laws, University of London; Lecturer on Evidence, Jurisprudence, and Private International Law at King's College, University of London; Joint Author of "The Law Relating to Company Promoters." In crown 8vo, cloth gilt .... **3s. 6d. net.**

Pitman's Handbook of Local Government Law. By J. Wells Thatcher, of the Middle Temple, Barrister-at-Law. In large crown 8vo, cloth gilt, 250 pp. .... **3s. 6d. net.**

Local Government Case Law, 1910 and 1911. By Randolph A. Glen, M.A., LL.B. (Cantab.), Barrister-at-Law of the Middle Temple and Western Circuit. In two volumes. Vol. I (1910), 176 pp., large crown 8vo, cloth gilt, **5s. net.** Vol. II (1911), about 350 pp., large crown 8vo, cloth gilt, **7s. 6d. net.**

SHORTHAND

TWENTIETH CENTURY EDITIONS

Phonographic Teacher. A Guide to a Practical Acquaintance with the Art of Phonography or Phonetic Shorthand. By Sir Isaac Pitman. Contains 70 reading and writing exercises.......... **6d.**
Key to the "Phonographic Teacher.".......... **6d.**
Exercises in Phonography. A Series of Graduated Sentence Exercises, illustrating the Principles of the Art as developed in the "Phonographic Teacher.".......... **1d.**
Progressive Studies in Phonography. Edited by Sir Isaac Pitman. Tenth Edition. **1s.**; cloth.......... **1s. 6d.**
Pitman's Shorthand Writing Exercises and Examination Tests. In crown 8vo, 240 pp., quarter cloth, **1s.**; cloth.......... **1s. 6d.**
Key to "Pitman's Shorthand Writing Exercises and Examination Tests." Contains Keys in Engraved Shorthand to all the Exercises. Complete Edition. In crown 8vo, cloth, 297 pp.......... **3s. 6d.**
Also in parts. Part I (to halving principle), **2s.** Part II.......... **2s.**
Pitman's Shorthand Instructor. A Complete Exposition of Sir Isaac Pitman's System of Phonography This is the Standard Instruction Book on Pitman's Shorthand There are 106 Reading and Writing Exercises and full Index Cloth, coloured edges, 248 pp. **3s. 6d.**
Key to "Pitman's Shorthand Instructor." **1s.**; cloth.......... **1s. 6d.**
Pitman's Shorthand Manual (being Part I of "Pitman's Shorthand Instructor"). **1s. 6d.**; cloth.......... **2s**
Key to "Pitman's Shorthand Manual".......... **6d**
Pitman's Shorthand Gradus; A Series of Writing Exercises for use with "Pitman's Shorthand Manual" or "Pitman's Shorthand Instructor" (Part I).......... **2d.**
Pitman's Shorthand Reporter (being Part II of "Pitman's Shorthand Instructor"), an adaptation of Sir Isaac Pitman's System to Verbatim Reporting. **2s.**; cloth.... **2s. 6d.**
Key to "Pitman's Shorthand Reporter".......... **6d.**
Reporting Exercises; A Praxis on the Grammalogues, Contractions, Phrases, etc., of the Reporting Style of Pitman's Shorthand.......... **6d.**
Key to "Reporting Exercises"; in the Reporting Style of Pitman's Shorthand.......... **1s.**
Pitman's Shorthand Commercial Course. Contains a presentation of Sir Isaac Pitman's system specially adapted for students who desire a knowledge of Shorthand for commercial correspondence. Cloth, 240 pp.......... **3s. 6d.**
Also published in parts, quarter cloth. Part I (Lessons 1 to 27, to halving principle), **1s. 6d.**; Part II (Lessons 28 to 40).......... **2s.**
Key to "Pitman's Shorthand Commercial Course." Contains Keys to all the Exercises and Business Letters. Cloth.......... **1s. 6d.**
Additional Exercises for "Pitman's Shorthand Commercial Course." Quarter cloth.... **1s.**
Pitman's Shorthand Primer. For Use in Elementary Day Schools and Evening Classes. In three books. Each.......... **6d.**
Key to "Pitman's Shorthand Primer." Books I, II, and III. Each.......... **6d.**
Pitman's Shorthand Reading Lessons, No. 1. For use with "Primer, Book II".......... **6d.**
Key to "Pitman's Shorthand Reading Lessons, No. 1.".......... **2d.**
Pitman's Shorthand Reading Lessons, No. 2. For use with "Primer, Book II".... **9d.**
Key to "Pitman's Shorthand Reading Lessons, No. 2.".......... **2d.**
Pitman's "Fono" Head-Line Shorthand Copy Books. Books A, B, C for "Teacher"; Nos. 1, 2, 3 for "Primer," Book I. Issued in copy-book size, fcap. 4to (8¾ in. by 6½ in.). Each.......... **2d.**
Graduated Tests in Pitman's Shorthand.......... **6d.**
Talks with Shorthand Students. By James Hynes. 111 pp. **1s.**; cloth.......... **1s. 6d.**
Pitman's Examination Notes on Shorthand. By H. W. B. Wilson. (6½ in. by 3½ in.) Cloth.......... **1s.** net.
Grammalogues and Contractions from "Pitman's Shorthand Reporter"; for use in classes.......... **2d.**
Vest Pocket List of Grammalogues and Contractions of Pitman's Shorthand. 2¾ in. by 1¾ in., 48 pp., limp cloth.......... **2d.**
Compend of Phonography. Containing alphabet, brief rules, etc.......... **1d.**
Pitman's Shorthand Dictionary. By Sir Isaac Pitman (Inventor of Phonography, a System of Phonetic Shorthand based on the Sounds of Speech and the Science of Phonetics). Ninth Edition. The size of the "Dictionary" is crown 8vo (7¼ in. by 5¼ in.), and it consists of 316 pp., in strong binding. Cloth.......... **4s.**
"Library Edition," roan, coloured edges.......... **5s.**

Pitman's Abridged Shorthand Dictionary. The size is royal 32 mo ($3\frac{1}{8}$ in. by $4\frac{3}{4}$ in.), and the corners are rounded. Roan, gilt edges....2s. 6d.
Student's Pocket Shorthand Dictionary. Same size as the "Abridged." Cloth....1s. net.
Reporters' Assistant. A Key to the Reading of the Reporting Style of Phonography, and a Course of Lessons in Shorthand Outlines. By Sir Isaac Pitman. Revised and enlarged. Eighth Edition. **1s. 6d.**; cloth....**2s.**
Phonographic Phrase Book. By Sir Isaac Pitman. Revised and enlarged. **1s.**; cloth, **1s. 6d.**
Legal Phrase Book....**6d.**
Insurance Phrase Book....**6d.**
Banking Phrase Book....**6d.**
Military Phrase Book....**1s.**

PITMAN'S SHORTHAND WRITERS' PHRASE BOOKS AND GUIDES

Electrical Engineering. Cloth....**1s. 6d. net.**
Shipping. Cloth....**1s. 6d. net.**
Railway. Cloth....**1s. 6d. net.**
Estate Agents, etc. Cloth....**1s. 6d. net.**
Printing and Publishing. Cloth....**1s. 6d. net.**

Other books in preparation.

Technical Reporting. Comprising Phonographic Abbreviations for Words and Phrases commonly met with in reporting Legal, Scientific, and other Technical subjects. By Thomas Allen Reed. Fifth Edition. **1s. 6d.**; cloth....**2s.**
Interlined Speed Practice Books. Containing ordinary print counted for testing speed, with alternate ruled lines for writing the shorthand. No. 1—Speeches. No. 2—Sermons. No. 3—Commercial....**1½d.** each; post free **2d.**
Keys to "Interlined Speed Practice Books," Nos. 1, 2, and 3. In Reporting Style. Each **2d.**
Graduated Dictation Books, for acquiring speed in Shorthand. In ordinary print. The reading matter is divided for speeds of 40, 50, 60, 80, 100, 120, and 160 words per minute. No. 1—Political Speeches. No. 2—Sermons. No. 3—Commercial. No. 4—Speeches (Commercial) and Addresses. In crown 8vo. Each....**4d.**
Key to "Graduated Dictation Book in Shorthand, No. 1." Ditto No. 2. In Reporting Style Each....**6d.**
Brief Reporting Notes in Shorthand, or Shorthand Dictation Exercises. Including Key in ordinary print. In demy 8vo. **6d.**; cloth....**1s.**
Pitman's Reporting Practice. A Manual of Dictation Exercises for the use of Shorthand Teachers and for Students cultivating Speed in Shorthand. In crown 8vo, cloth....**2s.**
Pitman's Progressive Dictator. Third Edition. In crown 8vo, cloth....**2s. 6d.**
Pitman's Shorthand Candidate's Dictation Exercises. In crown 8vo, cloth....**1s.**
Pitman's Speed Tests and Guide to Rapid Writing in Shorthand. In crown 8vo, cloth, 240 pp. **2s. net.**
Pitman's Cumulative Speller and Shorthand Vocabulary. By Charles E. Smith. In crown 8vo, cloth....**1s. 3d.**
Pocket Dictation Books, Nos. 1, 2, 3, and 4. Containing Speeches, etc., in ordinary print, counted in 10's for dictation. $2\frac{5}{8}$ in. by $3\frac{7}{8}$ in. Each....**2d. net.**
Acquisition of Speed in Shorthand, with Facsimile Notes of Famous Fast Writers of Pitman's Shorthand. Revised and Enlarged Edition. By E. A. Cope. In ordinary print. In crown 8vo....**6d.**
Shorthand in the Office. A Complete Shorthand Clerk's Guide, with chapters on Special Preparation, Aids and Hindrances, etc. By A. Kingston. Eighth Edition. **1s. 6d.**: cloth....**2s.**
Shorthand Commercial Letter Writer. A Guide to Commercial Correspondence in the Reporting Style. **1s.**; cloth....**1s. 6d.**
Key to the "Shorthand Commercial Letter Writer." Containing all the letters of the Shorthand Commercial Letter Writer. In ordinary print. **6d.**; cloth....**1s.**
The Shorthand Commercial Letter Writer and Key, in one volume. Cloth....**2s.**
Office Work in Shorthand. Being specimens of Legal and other Professional Work commonly dictated to Shorthand Clerks, in the Reporting Style. **1s.**; cloth....**1s. 6d.**
Key to "Office Work in Shorthand." Containing all the Letters, etc., of Office Work in Shorthand, in ordinary print. **6d.**; cloth....**1s.**
Office Work in Shorthand and Key, in one volume. Cloth....**2s.**
Business Correspondence in Shorthand. In the Reporting Style. **1s.**; cloth....**1s. 6d.**
Key to "Business Correspondence in Shorthand." In ordinary print, with the letters counted for dictation. **6d.**; cloth....**1s.**
Business Correspondence in Shorthand and Key. In one volume, bound in cloth....**2s.**
Exercises in Business Shorthand. By A. Benjamin. In foolscap 8vo....**1s. net.**
Trade Correspondence in Shorthand. In the Reporting Style....**1s.**
Key to "Trade Correspondence in Shorthand." In ordinary print, with the letters counted for dictation....**6d.**

Miscellaneous Correspondence in Pitman's Shorthand. Legal, Banking, and Commercial Letters, 250 words each. Reporting Style, with Key in ordinary print. In crown 8vo, oblong. Quarter cloth, **1s.**; cloth .... **1s. 6d.**

Miscellaneous Readings in Pitman's Shorthand, No. 1. In crown 8vo, 61 pp., cloth, **1s.** net; paper .... **8d.** net.

Pitman's Shorthand Teacher's Handbook. Fifteenth Edition. In crown 8vo. Cloth .. **1s. 6d.**

SHORTHAND READING BOOKS

(Printed from engraved characters except where otherwise stated)

In the Learner's Style

Æsop's Fables. In words of one syllable .... **6d.**

Easy Readings. In words of one syllable, with Key in ordinary print .... **6d.**

Learner's Shorthand Reader. Illustrated .... **6d.**

In the Corresponding Style

Phonographic Reader. A Course of Reading Exercises, with Key in ordinary print ...... **6d.**

The Chimes. By Charles Dickens. **1s. 6d.**; cloth .... **2s.**

The Battle of Life. By Charles Dickens. **1s.**; cloth .... **1s. 6d.**

Mugby Junction and Other Stories. By Charles Dickens. **1s. 6d.**; cloth .... **2s.**

Self-Culture. Intellectual, Physical, and Moral. A vade mecum for young men and students. By J. S. Blackie. **1s.**; cloth .... **1s. 6d.**

Key to ditto, in ordinary print. In post 8vo, cloth .... **2s. 6d.**

The Vicar of Wakefield. By Oliver Goldsmith. Illustrated. **2s.**; cloth .... **2s. 6d.**

Gulliver's Voyage to Lilliput. By Jonathan Swift. **1s.**; cloth .... **1s. 6d.**

Robinson Crusoe. By Daniel Defoe. Illustrated. **2s.**; cloth .... **2s. 6d.**

Tales and Sketches. By Washington Irving; with Key in ordinary print. **1s.**; cloth, **1s. 6d.**

The Silver Ship of Mexico. **1s.**; cloth .... **1s. 6d.**

A Shorthand Birthday Book of Dickens Quotations. Cloth (5 in. by 4 in.) .... **2s.** net.

Select Readings, No. 1 .... **6d.**

Select Readings, No. 2 .... **6d.**

The Book of Psalms. From the Authorised Version of the Bible. **1s.**; cloth .... **1s. 6d.**

In the Reporting Style

A Christmas Carol. By Charles Dickens. **1s.**; cloth .... **1s. 6d.**

The Cricket on the Hearth. By Charles Dickens. **1s. 6d.**; cloth .... **2s.**

The Haunted Man. By Charles Dickens; with 23 illustrations by S. J. Loxton. **1s. 6d.**; cloth **2s**

Tales from Dickens. 17 illustrations by P. Hudson. **1s. 6d.**; cloth .... **2s.**

The Sign of Four. By Sir A. Conan Doyle. **1s. 6d.**; cloth **2s**

Around the World in Eighty Days. By Jules Verne, abridged. **1s. 6d.**; cloth .... **2s.**

Selections from American Authors. With Key in ordinary print. **1s.**; cloth ...... **1s. 6d.**

The Legend of Sleepy Hollow. By Washington Irving; with Key in ordinary print .... **6d.**

Rip Van Winkle. By Washington Irving; with Key in ordinary print. Three illustrations .... **6d.**

Thankful Blossom. By Bret Harte. **1s.**; cloth .... **1s. 6d.**

Gleanings, No. 1. With Key in ordinary print .... **6d.**

Gleanings, No. 2. With Key in ordinary print .... **6d.**

The Holy Bible. Containing the Old and New Testaments. Lithographed in the Easy Reporting Style. Authorised Version. In demy 8vo (8¼ in. by 5⅝ in.), 800 pp., with table of contents. Cloth, red edges, **10s.**; roan, gilt edges, **12s.**; morocco, gilt edges, **15s.**

The New Testament. In Easy Reporting Style, with two coloured maps. Authorised Version. Size of page, 6¼ in. by 4 in. Roan, red edges, **4s.**; morocco, gilt edges .. **5s.**

The Book of Common Prayer. Easy Reporting Style. Size of pages, 6¼ in. by 4 in. Roan, red edges, **4s.**; morocco, gilt edges .... **5s.**

Church Services. Easy Reporting Style, 935 pp. Size of page, 6¼ in. by 4 in. Roan, bevelled boards, gold lettered back and side, **5s. 6d.**; morocco ditto, gilt edges .. **7s. 6d.**

Adaptations of Phonography to Foreign Languages

Dutch Phonography. An adaptation of Phonography to the Dutch language, by F. de Haan. In Dutch. In large post 8vo .... **5s.**

French Phonography. By T. A. Reed. Rules in English; Examples, etc., in French. Third Edition. **1s.**; cloth .... **1s. 6d.**

French Shorthand Commercial Correspondence. A Series of Business Letters in the French Phonography of Thomas Allen Reed. With Key. Cloth .... **1s. 6d.** net

German Shorthand. An adaptation of Phonography to the German language. In German and English. In crown 8vo. **1s. 6d.**; cloth .... **2s.**

Italian Phonography. An adaptation of Phonography to the Italian language, by Giuseppe Francini. In Italian. In crown 8vo .... **2s. 6d.**

Latin Phonography. An adaptation of Phonography to the Latin language, by Rev. W. Tatlock, S.J. In Latin. Cloth .... **2s. 6d.**

Spanish Shorthand. An adaptation of Phonography to Spanish. In Spanish. Fourth Edition. Cloth..**3s. 6d.**
Key to " Spanish Shorthand." Containing Key to all the exercises....................**2s.**
Welsh Shorthand. An adaptation of Phonography to Welsh. By Rev. R. H. Morgan. Third Edition. Re-written and improved by D. W. Evans....................**2s.**

TYPEWRITING

Pitman's Typewriter Manual. A Practical Guide to Commercial, Literary, Legal, Dramatic, and all classes of Typewriting work. Sixth Edition, Revised and Enlarged. In large post 4to, cloth..**2s. 6d.**
Pitman's Typewriting Examples. Forty-eight facsimile examples, embracing a variety of typewriting work—Commercial, Legal, Tabular, and General—on 24 cards in stout envelope. Can be used with any machine. In fcap. folio....................**2s. 6d.**
Ditto. Printed in oblong note-book for standing by the side of the machine ....**2s.**
Ditto. Note-book form, in covers ....**1s. 6d.**
Pitman's Exercises and Tests in Typewriting. More than 80 graduated exercises and over 40 examination tests. Second Edition, Revised. In fcap. folio. Quarter cloth, **2s. 6d.**; cloth..**3s.**
Practical Course of Touch Typewriting. With Chart and Diagram in five colours, Exercises and Repetition Practice. By C. E. Smith; 8½ in. by 11 in. English Edition, entirely re-set and revised. ADAPTED FOR USE WITH SINGLE OR DOUBLE KEYBOARD MACHINES **1s. 6d.** net.
How to Teach Typewriting. By Kate Pickard, B.A. (Lond.). In crown 4to, cloth..**3s.** net.
The Junior Typist. By Annie E. Davis. Designed as a guide through the elementary stages and thence to a first examination. In demy 8vo, cloth....................**1s.** net.
Remington Typewriter Manual. (FOR Nos. **5** and **7** and **10** and **11**.) With numerous Exercises and Illustrations and Examination Tests. Eighth Edition. In large post 4to. **1s.**; cloth ....**1s. 6d.**
Instructions on the Remington Typewriter. (Nos. **5** and **7**.) ....**6d.**
Instructions on the Bar-Lock. (No. **12**.)..**6d.**
Instructions on the Yost. (No. **10**.)..**6d.**
Instructions on the New Century Caligraph..**6d.**
Modern Typewriting and Manual of Office Procedure. A Reference Book for Professional Typists and Text-book for Students. By A. E. Morton. Fifth Edition. Size of page, 6½ in. by 9½ in. Over 100 illustrations..**2s. 6d.**
Practical Typewriting and Examination Guide. By A. E. Morton. ....**2s. 6d.**
Pitman's Backing Sheet for the Typewriter. Can be used with any cylinder machine. 9 in. by 13 in..**2d.**

PERIODICALS

Pitman's Journal. Subscription, which may begin at any time, **6s. 6d.** per annum, post free. (Estab. 1842). 32 pp. Weekly **1d.**, by post **1½d.**
Pitman's Shorthand Weekly. (Est. 1892). Weekly **1d.**, by post **1½d.**
Pitman's Commercial Teacher's Magazine. 32 pp., Monthly ....**1d.**
Book-keepers' Magazine. Edited by F. J. Mitchell. Organ of the Association of Book-keeping Teachers. Monthly, **2d.**; post-free **2½d.**
Commercial Teacher. Edited by W. H. Lord and H. H. Smith. Organ of the Incorporated Society of Commercial Teachers. Quarterly, **3d.**; post-free, **4d.**
Local Government Review. Monthly..**1s.** net.
Institute of Commerce Magazine. Edited by Egbert P. Booth. Monthly, **2d.**; post-free, **2½d.**
Hallett's Shorthand Gazette (Est. 1906) (Incorporating the " Phonographer "). Edited by F. J. Hallett. In royal 8vo. Monthly..**3d.**
Phonographic Monthly (Est. 1897). Edited by Al. Munro-Peebles. Illustrated. In royal 8vo. Monthly ....**2d.**
Phonographic Observer (Est. 1911). Edited by John Lanyon. In royal 8vo. Monthly..**3d.**
Reporters' Journal (Est. 1875), with which is incorporated the " Shorthand Magazine," founded in 1866. Edited by H. H. Lauenstein. Illustrated. In royal 8vo. Monthly, **4d.**; post free..**5d.**
Reporters' Magazine (Est. 1880). Edited by F. J. Hallett. Illustrated. In royal 8vo. Monthly, **4d.**; post free, **5d.**; yearly....................................**4s. 6d.**
Shorthand Teacher's Magazine. Organ of the Society of Certificated Teachers of Shorthand. Edited by V. W. E. Brooks. In demy 8vo. Quarterly, **3d.**; post free............**4d**

LTD